Tales of
Ayrshire

Also by Anna Blair

A TREE IN THE WEST
THE ROWAN ON THE RIDGE
QUEST

Tales of Ayrshire

Collected and retold by
ANNA BLAIR

SHEPHEARD-WALWYN

Illustrated by the Students of Marr College, Troon,
under the guidance of William B. Taylor

This edition first published 1983 by
Shepheard-Walwyn (Publishers) Ltd,
26 Charing Cross Road (Suite 34),
London WC2H 0HY

ISBN 0 85683 068 2 *cased*
0 85683 069 0 *limp*

Printed and bound in Great Britain by The Camelot Press Ltd,
Southampton, from photo-composition by
Alacrity Phototypesetters, Banwell Castle, Weston-super-Mare

To the good folk of Ayrshire
past and present
who have helped me write this book

Acknowledgements

I wish to record my thanks for the invaluable assistance, in their various fields of expertise, of the following friends:
Miss Barbara Graham of the Kilmarnock and District History Group; Mr. Robert Kirk, Historian of Dundonald; Mrs I.R. Mackie, author of *The Montgomerie Family*; Mrs Jennifer Ogilvie of Clarkston, and Mr. John Milligan of Dreghorn.

I also acknowledge a debt of gratitude to the Librarians of Ayrshire; those who have told me their tales; those who told me where I might find others; and those who lent me their precious volumes about old days in Ayrshire.

And I must record particular thanks to Mr. H.G.A. Anderson, formerly of University of Strathclyde, for painstaking and committed secretarial and advisory work; to Mr. William Taylor, his staff and art students at Marr College, Troon, who have provided the delightful illustrations in this book; to the Publisher whose advice and attention have been much appreciated; and finally to the most helpful, good-humoured and patient of husbands.

A.B.
Giffnock 1983

Contents

Introduction

The first requirement in writing a book of this kind is to decide just what belongs in it and, while leaving oneself some scope for interesting diversions, to keep fairly strictly to that plan. It seemed to me that legend, story, lore and tradition all merited place and that the final collection should contain a variety of such material.

The second step must be to find enough tales of all four categories to make a balanced whole, representing as far as possible all parts of the relevant area (in this case, Ayrshire). And a third consideration is whether to tell the facts behind each story, or simply to leave it as it stands, without writing-in the maybes and the maybe-nots! I decided to give some of the additional information in the form of foot-notes where these explained more fully a reference in the tale, or added to it something of interest.

Readers will realise from the text that Ayrshire, like Yorkshire, has been traditionally divided into thirds, Carrick in the South, Kyle in mid-Ayrshire and Cuninghame to the North. The map shows these divisions and most of the towns and villages from which the stories originated.

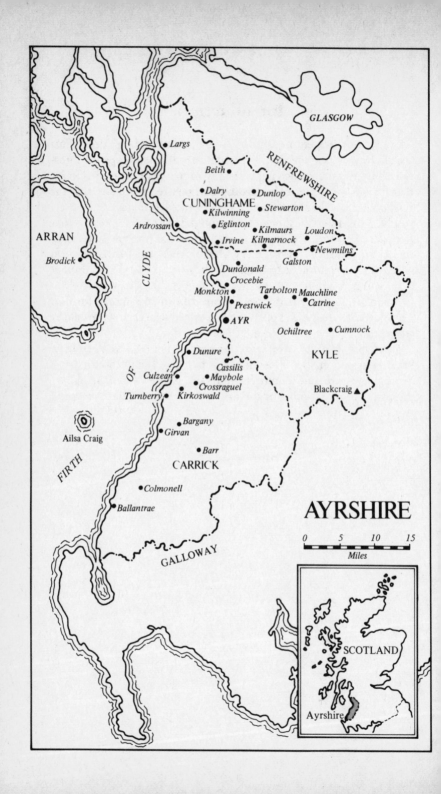

The Legend of Dundonald Castle

Back in the mist years before time was documented and tidied into history, there lived under an Ayrshire hill, a man named Donald, in a hollow beside a chittering burn. He lived with his busy little wife as had cheeks like blossom and as tended a trig and well-growing kailpatch, thick with vegetables and green curing herbs, and with even a row of pink and blue and yellow flowers edging the house where rush and daub walls met the dark soil. And there was, in the midst of her plot, the pride and joy of Libby Donald's heart, a little standing rock that had a tangle of orange-throated climbing-flowers rampaging over it, come every summer.

It was well that Libby was a practical body and a worker, for although Donald did a fair stint of labouring for the holder of a long rig, he was more given to meditating and even dreaming visions.

He was sitting over the turf ingle one night while his wife bustled about the room, poking rags into draught-cracks against the snell winds whetting in across the low lands from the sea and, as his wife bustled, Donald nodded over to sleep.

His dreams usually left him in the morning like snow in the sun as if they had never been, but the vision of that night was as vivid in the morning as it had been while he dreamed it. In it he saw himself led by a rainbow into a great town he knew was London and walking to a bridge over the River Thames. And the voice of his dream told him clearly that, if he went to the very middle of that bridge, good fortune would surely come of it.

In spite of the pleas and tears of his good little wife Donald set off staff in hand to seek the secret of his fortune. Many weary days he walked, and nights he tried to sleep in the lee of dyke or gable, or in caves he found in the high upland hills of the south, and at last he came to London town.

He found the very brig of his dream and right at the centre a dark dressed man with pale face gazing at the waters below. Surely, thought Donald, the Wizard of his fortune.

'You are wasting your time,' said the pale-faced man, 'for I have had the same vision, and I too was bid come here, where I would have a part in the finding of great wealth. And I know more than you, for in my dream there was described to me exactly the spot where the gold is to be found.'

Donald was disappointed after his long journey, though it seemed strange that he should have been misled by his dream.

'What is that place like?' he asked curiously, and to be polite.

'There was a hill, and I saw a man delving in a hollow under it beside a chittering burn where an apple-cheeked woman laboured in a cottage kailpatch. There were vegetables and green curing herbs and a row of pink and blue and yellow flowers growing by the cottage wall. In the middle of the garden there was a little standing stone with orange trumpet flowers growing over it. And where the man was delving is the spot where there lies the treasure. I think that man is myself and now all I must do is to find that place.'

Then Donald knew that *his* dream had not misled him, for the delving man was not this stranger, but himself ... the stranger was but his messenger, and the place was his very own kailpatch under the hill.

It took him only half the time to walk back home for he slept only every second night and louped the burns he had walked windingly alongside on the way.

It was summer when he reached the hill and the hollow and the apple-cheeked wife. The flowers were shining and the herbs grew green and healthy and Donald began to dig. In vain Libby scolded him for disturbing her growing things and piling soil on her neat paths; Donald dug his search holes all over the garden.

At last deep down beside the little standing stone his spade struck the corner of a kist and he eased it out. Inside was a fortune in gold and silver and jewels, and Donald was a happy man.

'But you've always been a happy man . . . what will you do with all your money?' said his sensible wife.

'I'll get a braw-fine castle built on the hill there and we can bide snug and happy here in our cot and watch it grow. And someday kings and queens and great lords and their ladies will live in it.'

So he did build his castle, stone upon great stone, and they said with never a nail pin in it. And time came when King Robert the Second and his court came there to live, and afterwards the Wallaces and the Earls of Dundonald who took their name from the cotman who lived in the hollow and followed the rainbow of his dream.

Although it is probable that Dundonald Castle was built in the time of Walter, the First High Steward of Scotland in the 12th Century, there was enough uncertainty about its origins to let this fanciful legend take root.

Saint Winning

Some time around the year 715 A.D. the holy Irish monk St. Winning came to live on the bank of the River Garnock. He founded a church there where, three hundred years later, the Abbey of Kilwinning was built.

He was visited at his first little church shortly after his arrival by a friend whose greatest pleasure was to walk in country places watching the birds and small animals of woodland, moor, riverbank and meadow. He was an expert angler too and talked of the many kinds of fish he had caught in his travels over Scotland and Ireland and across the north of England.

But the fish of the Garnock river eluded Winning's friend and during the whole of his stay he caught nothing. He was disappointed and complained to his host. St. Winning thereupon pronounced a curse on the river and in heavy rains that spring it changed its course and, from that day to this, has never gone back to its orginal bed.

St. Winning did not only curse, he took infinitely more pleasure in blessing, and it's told of him that he grieved so much over the sins of men that when he prayed at a particular spot between two rocks on a hummock by the river bank he wept such tears of sorrow over the many wickednesses he found among the people that a spring came forth between the rocks, clear, cold and sparkling, and blessed with great healing virtue. The halt, the blind and those stricken of speech, the sick and the dying were brought there to drink or even to bathe themselves in its waters. Many traditions have come down through the generations that numbers of them left again restored and whole.

The centuries crept on, Winning was long dead and other godly abbots and monks after him, and from time to time conduct in the monastery ran to such excesses and immoralities among the clergy that they lost their authority. Simple men paid them scant respect and even wealthy lairds no longer made them the offerings in money and kind that their predecessors had been given. The sick left off coming to the healing spring and took their ailments to holy places on other church lands. And the monastery clergy did not like the change.

Then one of the Fathers wrote a holy document in 1168 A.D. declaring that, a month before the recent wars began, the spring had warned of their outbreak with a gush of blood mingled in its flow. He thanked God that St. Winning's spring was once more a place of miracle and ordered that men should look to the Abbey again as their lives' authority.

There was at that time a simple lay brother who tended the Abbey garden and herded its beasts along the Garnock bank, where he enjoyed watching the reed-birds and water creatures and the flutter in the water of crow-foot flowers. He had thought in his high-minded youth that he was going among saintly men of wisdom and piety and was bewildered by the feasting, the quaffing and the sinful ongoings among certain of his fathers in God.

Now Brother John, the lowly shepherd, misdoubted that the Good Shepherd would invest His holy miracles in such unsaintly men and being a down-to-earth son of Ayrshire he poked sus-piciously about the spring to look into the cause or mechanics of its magic properties. But he had to shake his head when he saw nothing except what seemed to be the round-hole opening to the home of a tiny water-vole.

John, unlearned and out all day among his pastures was not to know that the fathers heard rumblings of coming wars again that summer and when water drawn from the spring ran red with blood again for eight days without cease, and great outbreaks of fighting followed within the month, he grew repentant and humble. He begged on his knees under open skies forgiveness for the sin of doubt and for judging his betters. For a time he poked no more about the spring and turned to taking greater care of his beasts; for while his attention had wavered, two or three of them had been lost to him.

But the years rolled on and many a time, as he grew in age and experience and as he lived out his lonely life of innocence among the beasts, he wondered at the planting of so holy a place of sign and prophecy, among the self-indulgent and paunchy Fathers of Kil-winning. But God knew best and maybe it was a mark of His favour on the other men of prayer and scholarship, the seekers after truth, who also lived there in John's time.

Six hundred years on, in the year 1826 another son of Kilwinning soil, a local worker, a man not unlike Brother John himself, was labouring on the ground at the side of the monastery, levelling the green sward there. His spade struck an ancient lead pipe, a knuckle's breadth in diameter, and curiously he followed its course as he dug. It ran from the building down to the well and he was a-thing puzzled

15

for it ran in steep descent and was certainly not for bringing water *up* from the spring to the Abbey. It was, more obviously, to send something down from Abbey to spring.

The labourer may have known something of the legend of blood in the spring water and wondered if that 'something' was blood from Abbey beasts or some other substance being used to convince the decent and simple folk of the Garnock valley of the evidence of local miracle and the prophesying power of the local clergy.

But he probably knew nothing of Brother John's puzzlement, at his finding of the hole of a water vole, and over the unexplained loss of certain of his sheep and goats.

The Vikings at Largs

In the mid-years of the 13th century the restless rovers of the Norselands were the sea-terrors of Western Europe. They pillaged and plundered, and set up defiant little chiefdoms even on the islands close to the west coast of Scotland. From there, where they dug themselves in as owners of the land they growled across the Minches and the sea-lochs, constantly threatening the mainland.

There was no king or warrior leader to growl back convincingly, no one to rally an army to rout them from the fringe lands of Scotland. Until, that was, the accession to the throne of the young King Alexander III. He was twenty-two when he began to assert Scotland's independence, assembling a powerful fleet and scouring the Western isles demanding either allegiance from the Norse who occupied them or their immediate withdrawal from lands so clearly Scottish. Some stayed as Alexander's vassals, some fled back home to take their complaints to Haco, the old warrior King of Norway.

Angered by the upstart young King of Scots, Haco, in his turn, mustered an army and prepared a great fleet to be ready by the summer of 1263 to teach Alexander a lesson.

Two traditional stories have come down the centuries since that spring and summer, telling of the expedition and its fate. There is the Norse one, sung by Sturla in 'The Raven's Ode', and the Scottish one told partly in the 'Ballad of Hardyknute' and partly by ancient record, relic and word of mouth.

THE TALE OF THE RAVEN'S ODE

In the summer of 1262 word came to the court of Norway of the routing of Norse chieftains in the Hebrides, of the ravaging by the Scots, of horrifying tales of men and women put to the sword, of razed homes, crops destroyed, churches sacked and even of children impaled on spears. It was a tale of torture, pillage and murder.

Enraged, Haco assembled his council and told them that such humiliation could not be borne without vengeance. They resolved on punishing attack. The months of winter were spent building galleys, preparing and repairing arms, and hardening their men.

Then one May morning at the port of Bergen, the brave fleet was assembled with the ageing Haco himself in the noblest ship. Each galley had twenty-seven rowing benches and around its sides, bright and glittering in the early summer sun of the northlands, were shields and steel spears and helmets. Their prows swept out and upwards into the heads of fierce golden dragons and over each of them fluttered a blood red flag with a black raven symbol in its centre. Proud men told of dreams of good omen ... one old Norseman told of warnings given long ago to the father of this Alexander by three saints. These three saints were St. Olaf of the Royal Robes, St. Magnus of Majestic Mein and St. Columba who, they said, was rough and ugly. The warnings to King Alexander II were that he should not go on some purposed voyage of conquest. The King chose to ignore the dreams with their prophecies of doom, and died on his expedition.

'Surely,' the dreamer said now, 'his son will also die, and we must go and see that that is so.'

Then sails were set, the elegant ships slipped out of the harbour and with the rythmic sweep of a thousand oars they bore westward to Orkney. They reached there by midsummer, then swept on to Caithness and into the Sound of Skye. On the way they paused here and there to make shore raids, leaving slain Scots, charred homes and wasted granaries behind them. Then Haco sailed his conquering fleet into the Firth of Clyde.

Messages flew back and forth between him and Alexander negotiating for the islands of Bute, Arran and the Cumbraes. But, at least in the bargaining, Haco met his match, for Alexander was not prepared to give up any of them. The Norsemen, hungry for battle, grew impatient and found a new way of annexing territory. They dragged some of their ships overland to Loch Lomond and ravaged shore and island cottages and mansions there. And Alexander grew angry.

Back in the Clyde firth sat the main Norse fleet, now beginning to rise and fall in a swell of water. Soon a wild mid-season storm had arisen and was buffeting the Dragon prows and great sails. The fleet was hit by battering winds and drenching spray, and began to scatter and drift towards Largs. Some were wrecked on the rocky Ayrshire coast. The King's ship dragged its anchor dangerously but held, and while the Norsemen were still fighting the storm to hold together, the Scots swarmed down the hill behind the shore, forward over the sand and on to the water's edge. They yelled war cries that curdled Viking blood and rained darts and spears on the beleaguered Norsemen in their galleys, and in the shallows of the sea's edge.

18

When darkness fell later in the evening, as suddenly as they had appeared, the Scots withdrew to rest the night, then to rearm and regroup. All night the Norse stood by the tide-line or in their ships waiting for another attack.

Next day the main battle was joined in earnest. Haco was impatient to be in the thick of it but he was counselled to stay on his own great galley where he could direct and rally his nine hundred steel-clad Vikings and stay alive to guide the victory and the triumphant journey home.

There were five hundred Scottish knights on horseback, in armour tempered and fashioned in Spain. Behind them were yeomen and spearmen. Forward they came again like a tide hurling itself in counter-waves against the sea and the fighting-men there. The Vikings broke ranks, leapt into their light boats and sklimmed back quickly to the main fleet in the bay. A challenge was thrown out then by the Scottish champion Fergus of the Jewelled Helmet for a Viking to meet him in single combat. Andrew Nikolsen took it up, smote the Scotsman through from casque to saddle and took Fergus's costly studded waist-belt and helmet by right of conquest.

The battle raged until the sun was westering over Arran, and Sturla sings in the Raven's Ode of the great victory that went that evening to the Vikings. Next day they gathered the spoils of war and bore their dead out into their ships for honourable burial. They sailed home by the Hebrides with the steady creak of rowlock and the swishing plash of oar blade.

But their Lord Haco would sail to fight no more, for he had suffered badly on the voyage, and like a true and bold Viking he died at sea. He had lain dying while his minstrel read to him from the Bible and from the chronicles of the mighty men who were his forebears, and then quietly turned his own brave face to the ship's side and lay still.

They took his body to lie at rest in St. Magnus Cathedral in Orkney, where vigil was kept over it until the following spring. Then it was carried over the sea again to Bergen where his son Prince Haco waited to do honour to his valiant father.

And that is the tale as it is told in the ballad of the Raven's Ode, a tale of Viking courage and victory.

THE TALE OF THE ANCIENT SCOTS

But Hardyknute and the Scottish Tradition has it differently and who is to say which is the more nearly true? If victory was to the brave Norsemen why was it that the Battle of Largs ended for ever Viking claims to the Western isles, and that the west of Scotland never saw Norse raiders again?

This is how Scottish bards and minstrels have told their version of the tale:

The Scots had struggled over many centuries to become united under a strong Scottish King and now with the young and lusty Alexander III on the throne it looked as if they had achieved nationhood. But whether they looked north or west around their coasts, the banners of the Vikings fluttered tantalisingly at their sea fringes. The islands echoed to the Norse tongue, sun glinted on Norse arms, and Norse galleys rose and fell on Scottish tides.

There was a constant drain on Alexander's energy and resources to keep these enemies at bay when there was still so much to be done to unify Scotland, to subdue its own rebels and contain the wild Highland clans. A peaceful kingdom was only a dream so long as the Norsemen threatened its soil. Alexander made up his mind that they must be ousted and sent scurrying home from his Western Isles. He gathered an army and prepared a small fleet. He sailed in and out of sea lochs and channels and sent small bands of marauding men ashore to spring-clean the off-shore islands. His strategy was quick, sharp and effective. The Norsemen were harried until they left their adoptive homes and fled north and east back home to clipe to Haco, about the fiery new King of Scots.

Meantime Alexander brought back his force and began to plan for the angry retaliation he knew would come from the doughty old warrior across the water. Haco had ruled his people for fifty years and minstrels sang of his prowess, even during his lifetime, in Viking halls and keeps and palaces. Alexander heard from mercenary spies (who made their dubious livelihood from tramping across western Europe and sailing in small cargo vessels to sell the secrets of one power to another) that Norwegian pines were being sent thudding to the ground around Bergen for galley timbers and that on sea-coasts hammers rang on adze and prow. He heard too, before spring had greenmantled the fiords in 1263, that Haco himself was on his way with a powerful fleet of oak and ash ships carved and gilded with shining gold decoration and carrying the finest warriors in the land.

Alexander too plundered his forests for shafts for the deadly long Scots-style spears, and sent to Spain for the finest breast-plates, helmets and leggings. And then he gathered and marched great armies from all airts of the lowlands to the Ayrshire coast.

There he waited for the Vikings to curl their force round the north of Scotland and sail the gold prows unhindered down the rugged coast. He made no move as the enemy fleet passed Skye and Islay. But there were keen watching eyes in the square tower of St. John's Church and the spies gave their alerting signal when the sails were sighted away to the north in the Firth of Clyde. Still Alexander did not make a move, not even when the Norse fleet sat anchored and rocking opposite the small town of Largs on the Ayrshire coast.

The people of Largs discreetly moved inland to the forest of Kyle and the hills beyond, to take cover from the impending battle, and both sets of fighting men honed themselves for conflict.

A party of the Vikings came ashore in small boats and made a quick assault on the Castle and, having shown a flash of their mettle, withdrew into the galleys and moved back to the shelter of the great Cumbrae.

Alexander had his weather eye on the equinoctial storms which would surely come within a few days, and played for time by opening negotiations with Haco for Lordship over Bute and Arran, neither of which he had the least intention of giving up. Messengers passed back and forth with claim and refusal as the days grew shorter and darker and the sea began to curdle and heave.

Then one autumn day in the shifting currents the Norse ships dragged their anchors and drifted towards the south end of Largs under the Haylie Brae. Alexander with his bowmen, horsemen, spearmen and armoured knights were poised and ready. They descended on the galleys drifting now in the shallows and harassed them until darkness fell. Then they withdrew to plan the next day's attack. In the morning the Battle of Largs was truly joined. The Norsemen left their ships to skeleton crews and waded shoulder to shoulder, targe to targe, towards the shore. There was a furious exchange of darts and spears, staffs shivered each other and axes felled brave men. But the Scots had the advantage of ground height and Haco's men were outpositioned and outnumbered and over-powered. They fell backwards as steadily as they had advanced, shoulder to shoulder, shield to shield. Tradition tells their losses at sixteen thousand souls and those of the Scots at five thousand.

Alexander, young and victorious, could afford to be chivalrous and allowed a party of Norsemen ashore for five days to bury some

21

of their dead and carry others back for a home voyage to Valhalla instead. Then the Scots watched the once-proud Viking ships sail off to the north again and they heard later of the death in the Orkneys of the disappointed old King of Norway.

And so Hardyknute and the old Scottish records give Alexander the victory noting the final clearance from his shores of the 'pirates' from Bergen.

In time a new Norse King married Alexander's daughter and their child became his heir. The days of Alexander III's reign were the Golden Years of Scotland's story and ended only when he was accidentally killed and, on her way to take his throne, his little grand-daughter the Maid of Norway, like her other grandfather, died in the Orkney Islands. Scotland then lay prey to other invaders than the Vikings of the North.

And all that remains now of the great battle at the town of Largs are a few place names that have survived the centuries, Camphill, Routdon Burn, Killingcraigs, a tumulus known as Haco's Tomb, and a memorial pillar called 'The Pencil'.

There is also a fine jewelled pin safe in an Edinburgh museum and known as the Hunterston Brooch. But its origin and legend are another story.

This story of the Battle of Largs is a marriage of the pro-Norse 'Sturla's Ode' and the pro-Scottish 'Ballad of Hardyknute'. The writer of 'Hardyknute' Elizabeth Halket, Lady Wardlaw, 1677-1727, laid her ballad in the tower of Fairlie Castle. The battle is its climax but it tells of much more than that. It tells of the part played by her fictitious warrior Hardyknute and his family before, during and after, the battle. Many of Lady Wardlaw's details of history, geography, distances and landmarks are inaccurate, but her version of the battle itself is popularly accepted and is deeply rooted in Ayrshire lore.

The Hunterston Brooch now in the Scottish Museum of Antiquities in Edinburgh, is a splendid piece five inches across, its silver filigree richly ornamented with 118 gold beads embedded among garnet and amber insertions. It was found near the site of the battle and was considered by Professor Finn Magnusson in 1846, to have been lost during the fighting, possibly by King Haco himself.

The Enchanted Saddle

Sir Fergus of Ardrossan was the last of the line of the Barclay family, a man famous in all the countries of Europe for his unfailing good fortune at the gaming-table and racing-course, and for the fleetness of his fine horses. The swiftness of these animals was so breathtaking that it came to be thought unearthly and that Sir Fergus's secret lay in an enchanted saddle he had had as a gift from his friendly intercourse with the Devil. It was universally believed that he had given his soul to Satan in exchange for success at the gambling and victory in any contest with his horses.

One day, having left his finest animal at the edge of a woodland to go shooting on foot among the trees, he came back to find his beautiful silver-trimmed saddle gone, and so enraged was he at the theft and so distressed, that he did not speak to a living soul for a week. The truth was, said suspicious rivals, that Fergus feared Satan's anger at his carelessness and trembled at what dreadful future lay in store, now that he was out of favour with his master. They waited to see his fortune change.

And change it did.

Sir Fergus had two children, a son by his loved first wife, a lad most precious and promising; and by his less-loved second wife a bonnie young daughter, in some danger of spoiling by her doting mother.

The boy would someday be as skilful a horseman as his father for he had sat the Ardrossan animals well since childhood, but he was young and to Sir Fergus's mind lacked wise judgement about the size and spirit of the mounts he wanted to ride. There was one beautiful chestnut, high, proud and handsome and which, as if to taunt those who slandered that he had truck with the Devil, Barclay called Lucifer. And it was young Barclay's dearest ambition to gallop Lucifer over the hill behind Ardrossan. But the horse was wild-tempered and sensitive, much too spirited for the boy to ride. Some months after the loss of his famous bridle and saddle, Sir Fergus had to make a long journey on a slow but sturdy mare, leaving Lucifer at home, along with his children and his second wife. He left also serious and grave warning that under no circumstances was his son to go near, far less mount, the chestnut horse.

Lady Barclay tolerated her stepson quite kindly. He was a lively, likeable youth and she was not a wicked woman. But she was the mother of Sir Fergus's only other child, the lass who was his second heir. Whether she encouraged or merely consented to young Barclay taking out the nervous horse the story does not tell, but his father was scarcely half-a-day's journey away from Ardrossan when a stable lad was persuaded to saddle the animal and lead it out to the courtyard.

The young rider had the most exultant and joyous hour of his life flying across the moors, thundering down the riverside, his long curls streaming out behind him. And then a loose stone flew up from Lucifer's hooves and terrified the horse so that it reared wildly and threw the lad on to the riverbank where his head struck a stone and he was killed.

When Sir Fergus came home and heard of the tragedy he was distracted, and grief-stricken, scarcely knowing what he did, he slew his wife who had allowed his son to ride Lucifer. Leaving his now motherless daughter he fled to Arran and there shut himself into the solitary Tower of Kildonan, with no company but a single servant-boy. And there he stayed, almost without comforts or possessions, for several long years.

He seldom left the Tower but one chill day in winter he went walking in a lonely place to find some extra kindling for their fire. There he met a gipsy woman, who looked strangely at him and offered to read his palm. He would have thrown her aside but something in her narrow eyes held him and he gave her his hand.

'Your hand tells of woe and sorrow, good Master,' she began. 'It tells that if you should ever set foot on Irish soil, then your death will be close at hand.'

Sir Fergus now had little wish to reach old age, but he laughed grimly at the gipsy all the same, for he had no links with Ireland across the water there, no kin, no business, no prospect of ever setting foot on Irish soil. He told her so, but she repeated her warning as if she had not heard.

It was a month later that Fergus ventured out once again from the keep, this time to find some fresh sea-weeds to make a pot of soup. He was abroad at daybreak walking along the deserted beach so that he would meet no one. He strode along over some turf sods laid out to dry along the shore, no doubt being prepared for making a house roof. Then he saw a fishing-boat at the jetty half-a-mile away so he

24

gathered a bundle of tangle from the tide-line and made quickly for the Tower before there were men from the boat ashore.

Over their broth that night the servant told him that the boat was Irish. She had brought a load of special turves for a bien Arran cotman over the hill and the crew had set them on the shingle for collecting.

Now Fergus of Ardrossan knew that his hour had come. He bade the young man take his body when he died, stitch it into a bullock's hide, and place it on the shore when the tide was out. In a few days he was dead of a fever and the loyal servant did as he was bidden, then retired to the flat dunes to watch over his strange master until the waves carried the body away.

The tale ends with the uncanny washing ashore of Sir Fergus de Barclay under the walls of his own castle at Ardrossan. His daughter, now a grown and gracious young woman had it taken up then and buried in the family chapel.

No one knows if any of his old rivals even cared, after all these years, whether they had been right or wrong about the Devil and Fergus Barclay's soul. By then they had turned their attention to another gambling laird who, like Ardrossan before him, had a stable of flying horses and a silver-traceried leather saddle uncommonly like the one stolen from Sir Fergus so many years before.

No one has recorded what gave rise to this legend of Sir Fergus Barclay, because he actually died at the Battle of Ardscoll and not in the melodramatic circumstances of 'The Enchanted Saddle'. It is true that he had no male heir but his daughter married a son of the House of Eglinton and took ownership of Ardrossan Castle with her into that family.

The Cadger
of Dunlop

The hair of the Dunlop cadger was grey and straggling thin, but no one ever knew him as anything but 'Young Robin'. The reason was, tradition says, that he had an appetite for his carting work like a man only a third of his age, and was always eager for the lion's share of whatever of such trade was going. At the time of this story he was not best pleased that two incomers by marriage to Dunlop bought carts and set out to rival him at his trade. The cadger had also a fine line in howff stories and kept many a coven of cronies so late over their stoups at the inn that they went home to wives, already abed, and lying there stiff in every joint with anger.

The usual cheerful sound of murmur and guffaw met Young Robin one dark night when he burst open the inn door and almost fell inside, his face drawn and smit with terror and his hands shaking in their need of a reviving glass or tankard to hold. When he had been plied with pacifying drinks (partly out of genuine good-heartedness, partly out of curiosity to know what was behind his distress) he obliged by relating the dreadful experience he had just been through.

He mopped his whey face, sat down alongside the other two cadgers and began in a trembling voice.

'It was like this, you ken, I was driving home from a delivery in Kilmarnock there just now, taking my time, for the mare had had a heavy pull into the town earlier on. And I was just by the bridge there when I saw, riding neck and neck beside me . . . och that's a rare word to use "neck and neck" . . . for it was a horseman,' his voice dropped . . . 'with no heid! I flicked on Annie's rump to leave him behind me, but I couldnae gain an inch. When I go'ed the faster, so did he himself . . . then I pulled up sudden-like to let him fly past me . . . but he didnae do that neither. It was just as if he was my shadow, making no noise at all with the animal's hooves on the stones or no cracking with his whip. Then when we reached the town, the headless man on his horse sprang up high in the air and vanished, aye, just as if he'd never been there, into a queer flare of fire that had no kindling and no

26

embers.' His story told, Young Robin groaned and trembled again.

His friends went home earlier than usual that night in twos and threes, glad to spend a safe hour with their dames.

But the spirit, whatever it was, had a witching on Young Robin and just a week later he was returning from another hauling journey, to Glasgow this time, and carrying a barrel of ale, when at a lonely spot near Camore in a clump of bushes close to the roadside ... 'a spot,' he told them in the alehouse when he arrived there, once again sweating with fear ... 'a spot where my grandfather used to tell me when I was a bairn, that the fairies held their merry meetings. I had just now reached this haunted spot when my ears were tingled with an eerie, sweet kind of music ... like a spell, you ken. And when I looked round I saw a whole army of fairy folk, as true as I'm sitting here ... and a' dressed in green like the grass and coming at me as if to put a glammer on me,' he shivered, 'Losh, but it wasnae canny! Annie was feart forbye and she ran off with the cart, and me hanging on the reins like it was one of yon chariots of Rome. Then the cart back-latch got loose, the ale barrel fell off and rumbled and birled back down the road. It stove in on the stones and the ale gushed out like a river and I lost every drop.'

Young Robin emptied his jar of ale and wiped his mouth nervously.

'My but I doubt I'll not be over my door slab this side Candlemas, for I think there's mischief aboot for them as cadges between Glasgow and Kilmarnock.'

It was odd though, that in the end it was not Young Robin who kept away from the Glasgow-Kilmarnock road with all its dangers. It was the incomer-cadgers. They had no wish to meet Dunlop's witches or warlocks or headless horsemen. They sold their new painted carts, put their horses out to grass and took up work at Greenside farm-steading, where Mistress Wilson made the best cheese in Dunlop and gave it to them thick with her baked farls. So they were pleased enough with their new lot and never really hankered after the cadging again. And Young Robin was pleased too. He fixed the back-plank, repainted his name on its sides and bravely shuttled between Glasgow and Kilmarnock and out the roads all sides from Dunlop, plying his trade unhindered by his rivals. From time to time (at judicious intervals) he fought off bogles and witches on his travels and, for all the rest of his carting life, he was the only man with courage enough to face them. And laddies who might have grown up to be cadgers found themselves content to take up safer occupations.

27

The Gems of May Culzean

Young Mistress May Culzean was her father's only child, heir to his fine castle with its tapestries and furnishings, its rich kists of gold and gems, with its broad fertile acres of countryside on three sides and the securing cliffs on the fourth. And so, even if she had not been fair and young with golden hair falling to her slender waist, she would have attracted suitors from all airts of Ayrshire and beyond.

Her fond father had indulged without spoiling her since her earliest years, and taken the greatest care of her throughout childhood with its small ailments and perils. But that care was nothing to the protection he lavished on her now that she was emerging as a young woman. For in that part of Carrick of late there had been a strange spate of tragedies in which young, comely, and not so comely, girls, all the daughters of wealth, had fallen to their deaths from a cluster of grey stones on the Bennane cliff-tops, with no explanation of just how such a series of coincidences had happened. Perhaps the girls had only been unfamiliar with the path. Now the spot was known sombrely as the Death Rocks.

The first few young knights who came courting May Culzean, however honourable and noble they may have been, were out-dwellers unknown to the family, and did not have good enough credentials to win her father's consent to going a-walking with her. After that there were one or two local lairds whose motives in paying their attentions seemed suspect to the parents at the Castle. And so it was with relief and pleasure that they finally welcomed Sir John of Carleton, a distant kinsman, who hailed from South Ayrshire himself and had everything to commend him as a prospective bridegroom. He was brave and bold, his family lineage went back into the mists of history and it was said of him that his merchant ventures gathered him an increase in gear and riches year after year. Such a man could surely cherish and protect a sheltered young girl as carefully as her own family and with even more wealth and luxury. May's father could not resist such qualities and happily gave his consent to Sir John to pay court to her. And May herself, it seemed, could not resist his other charms, his curling dark hair and handsome figure, his quick wit and the gracious compliments of a ready tongue.

They walked and talked and rode together and May Culzean was delighted with him. But she was a girl of spirit and had once or twice rebelled at her father's high-handed dismissal of suitors, the minstrel son of a baron who played under her window, the scholarly squire who sent her poems, and especially a fresh-faced gentle young knight she would have liked to know better. She ventured to voice her modest rebelliousness to Sir John Carleton and he seemed to understand. He spoke to her earnestly about it. Was this courtship of theirs not perhaps too easy? Did she think there was enough challenge in it? Her father was pleased, she herself was happy, and Sir John had not had to 'win' her at all. Would there not be more excitement to their romance, he wondered, if they eloped together? If they pretended they were going far away, carrying all their wordly wealth with them? They could find a country priest to join them man and wife, but of course they would come back home again soon, put their jewels back in the family kists, beg forgiveness and let the wedding feast go on as arranged.

May was delighted with the idea. She sang softly in her chamber and thrilled at the daring prospect of running off with Sir John. She draped four priceless strings of pearl, emerald, ruby and jade around her neck, put a choice gemmed ring on every finger and fastened inner and outer garments and even her silk snood, with heirloom brooches. All this finery she covered with the rich cloth-of-gold cloak her grandfather had had brought from the East for his lady. Then in the early morning, before dawn broke over Bennane, she slipped past the sleeping pantryman on his kitchen chaff and out to meet her lover at the stable-yard yett.

They rode into the frail morning light laughing softly at their adventure, May Culzean light-hearted and gay as she talked of their future together and rode before him on his mount.

Then of a sudden it seemed to the eloping bride that Sir John's arms around her as he held his reins were less gentle, and she let out a scolding cry at this change of touch. Then all at once he pulled in his mare so that it stood snorting and pawing the grass, he grasped his lady roughly, dismounted and stood her unceremoniously on the ground. And she saw in the mist of daybreak off the sea that she stood beside the Death Rocks with only the sturdy and now threatening figure of John of Carleton between her and a sheer drop over the cliffs.

'And now my bonnie Mary of Culzean, unfasten that cloth-of-gold and spread it at your feet; unwind these necklaces, unhand your precious rings, unpin the jewelled brooches, take off your silken shifts and petticoats and drop them into your costly cloak from the East. Then look your last on all of them for you will not need them in the cold seas.'

May trembled but she was made of sterner, quicker-witted stuff than those other ladies who had been here before her, ladies she now knew had lined Sir John's coffers by leaving their jewels and fine clothes behind them when they had hurtled to the rocks below. She gave a frightened cry and her small hands fluttered at her throat as she began to unfasten the clasp of her cloak. Then she paused.

'You are a false knight, Sir John Carleton, base and wicked and cruel. But you are a gentleman born and reared and must not watch a lady undress to her nakedness. Turn around false bridegroom, for you have surely not forgot your manners.'

It was true. The manners his nurse and lady mother had instilled were still habit with him and, exulting in the wealth he would shortly gather up, he turned his back, humouring her, and stood looking down on the sea pounding in on the dark rocks. May's hands no longer fluttered, they became small determined fists and, before John Carleton had tallied up the likely worth of her jewels, she promptly pushed him over the edge to join the souls of all such wicked men. Then she bundled up her baubles and led his mare back to her father's castle.

Some say that May Culzean had despised Sir John Carleton from the beginning of his courtship, suspecting that he was the killer of the other Carrick ladies. And they say that she planned their 'elopement' and its consequences as carefully as he had tried to do.

No one knows for sure, but not many months later the fresh-faced young and gentle knight, who had come a-wooing before, came again, with nothing to offer but his poverty besides a brave and loving heart, and won Mistress May from a contented father who was glad to welcome the young man as his son.

There are various versions of this old tale in prose and ballad. This one is a combination of the features common to most of them, including its setting at Gamesloup near Bennane. The 'feel' of the ballad may be had from this verse,

O turn ye round, the false Sir John
O turn ye round, quoth she,
It ne'er became a gentleman
A naked lass to see.

and, like other sources, it finishes the tale by telling how the fair May pushed him over the cliff and watched him circle slowly head over heels to the rocks below.

Seal Bride

There are twists and turns of the legend of the Seal Bride related in a dozen seashore villages up and down the Atlantic coast of Scotland but this one was told of a rocky bay not far from the small Carrick town of Ballantrae.

The hero-man of the tale was young and ruddy, a fisherman who loved the sound and sight of the seas along the coast from Ardstinchar castle to Lendalfoot. It's said that he wandered there often of an evening and that one summer night he saw the head of a seal, gleaming wet and brown in the waters lapping round a row of rocks. As the tide rose and spumed over the rocks he saw, with a strange fearful shiver of excitement, that it was not an ordinary seal but one of the seal-women he had heard tell of, and never believed in, since he was a bairn. She lay on one of the high humped rocks singing now, and eagerly he waded out to look on her. She lay dreaming, exulting in the cold clean spray, her seal-coat at her side to slip on at will and her beautiful human form golden skinned and rose-tipped. Her eyes were soft and shining in the glow of sunset rippling across the waters of the bay. And, simple as simple, he fell in love with her.

Raised on the shoreman's lore of seawitches, he remembered now that to win her and keep her he must withold the sealskin from her and never let her have it back. And so he trod the last of the waves that separated them, making less noise than the singing sea, and gathered up the soft brown coat before she knew he was there. Then gently he touched her, wakened her from her dreams and earnestly, and with the sun now on his tanned handsomeness, he begged her to be his wife.

She was lost now anyway to the deep underworld of the sea without her coat, but the love in the young man's face might have won her anyway and she agreed to marry him.

She loved her kindly tender husband and was true and faithful to him for a long time. But there came days when she was often sad and lonely for her other family among the sea-folk. As she walked along the shore or sat by the fireside of their fisher cot she would hear their forlorn singing, mourning their loss of her. The sound would float across to her when a soft mournful wind blew in from the rocks and she would wonder how they fared and what they thought had

31

become of her. And sometimes she was sore tempted to wonder too where her man had hidden her sealskin.

More and more often she was tempted so, and then one night she had a dream that he had folded it in a shawl and laid it above the loose planks of the cottage ceiling. Next day she busied herself about the house so that she would not think too much about the coat. But she dreamed the same dream a second and a third night. The day after the third dream, with trembling hands she moved the planks about until she did indeed come on the soft feel of her own furskin coat. She drew it down and slipped it over her shoulders and a terrible sweet longing came on her to be swimming in the sea. She ran down to the shore line and into the water and swam deeper and deeper into the clean green waters, with greater and greater joy in the swimming, and each time her brown head broke the surface her singing spread hauntingly over the water.

For a month the heart-broken young husband searched the sea-shore every day and every night for his wife. Then one evening he found an empty sealcoat lying on the seaweed above the tideline, and he put it on. The sea now drew him too and he swam down and down until he found the mer-country of the kindly brown seal-people and, living there among them, his dear wife.

She had almost forgotten his love and tenderness and what a braw lad he was, but now once again she fell in love with him and they came home to live together in their cottage.

The seasons turned, year died behind year and the house rang with the laughter of the bairns she had borne to him. The seal woman was too busy to long for her old life but by and by as they grew older she began to smell the tangy smell of the sea-world and to wonder about the seal-folk. The old dream came again too, she searched for her seal-coat and found it this time in the thatch.

Again she slid into the water and swam away to a joy and peace she had never truly known on land. Surely, she missed her gudeman and her five bairns but every Sunday evening for six weeks she swam up to the rocks by the shore and laid a sealskin there. Six skins there were and when the fisherman had gathered them together he gave one each to four of his children and kept one for himself. The sixth skin was for his eldest son, who was from home looking for the farmwork he wanted to do instead of the fishing. They waited for him till they could wait no longer then they left his skin on a rock, so that when he came, he would find it and follow them. Then they looked at their cot home for the last time and went off with their father to join their beloved mother and learn to live and splash and play in their green sea-world.

Day after day they came back to see if the sixth seal skin was gone but still it lay on the rock waiting for their brother to claim it.

But that eldest boy had by now found *his* heart's desire and was working on the land, delving and planting and looking to the day when the soil under his hand would flush with green then gold. He had no longing in him for the sea. He too watched the seal-skin from the hills behind Ballantrae, he watched while the salt seas washed over it and the hot sun shone on it until at last it fell apart and floated away altogether. Then he felt that he was free to be his own man.

He married one of the pretty milkmaids at the laird's house and in time told the story to his children, of their seal grandparents and uncles and aunts. They all laughed and did not believe him, but he watched them carefully lest any wandered too near the rocks where their kin-cousins still frolicked in the shallows there.

The Legend of the Auld Brig of Ayr

Two sisters sat alone one stormy October day of 1263 in a castle keep near St. John's Church in Ayr. They were trembling like the rest of Ayr's good citizens at tidings that the fleet of Haco, the King of the Norsemen with his Viking warriors was lying off the Cumbraes at Largs, having moved there from the Bay of Ayr. The sisters, Marian and Mary Craufurd, were young, beautiful and wealthy and faithfully in love with two knights of the Scottish King's force, waiting with Alexander III to do battle with the fierce Norsemen.

The King was young and bold and Richard de Boyle of Kelburn and Sandy Fraser were young and bold too, the flower of Scottish chivalry. While the sisters loved them for their spirit and courage they feared for their lads when they were in battle.

That morning they had sent Allan Boyd, one of their servants, to Largs to bring back news of what was happening ... whether the two sides still stalked each other, snarling, or had finally joined battle. Now the sisters took turns of watching from their chamber window to see him when he rode home again.

At last Boyd came, waving his bonnet joyfully as he rode, then throwing his reins to a stable-lad, he ran upstairs two steps at a time bringing good word to his ladies that Haco was defeated and his fleet scattered. The battle had raged on land, in the shore shallows and farther out too in the deeps all along the coast from Knock Castle to Portencross. But it had been at its height at Largs where Alexander had led the final onslaught himself. Richard of Kelburn and Sir Sandy Fraser had covered themselves with glory and been saluted even by the enemy.

Mistress Marian gave good Allan Boyd a purse of gold and Mistress Mary drew down his rough cheek and kissed it gratefully.

'Make ready the greatest banquet ever held here in this castle,' Marian told him.

'Bring out the best wines, throw on the sweetest-smelling logs and turn the spit, for our lords will surely make back to us here with all speed,' ordered Mary, and then paused with head bowed, rosary in hands, for a word of prayer to the good Lord for keeping safe their menfolk.

34

And home towards Ayr the young knights rode to the beautiful and loving women waiting for them in the castle, the squalling wind following them from Largs, and then through a rising storm of battering, deluging rain and blatting winds. The River Ayr rose and seeped on to the banks, breaking them down here and there, all along a hundred ell length. The torrent surged and foamed cream: and commonsense paused the two knights briefly. But love was on the other side, they were light-hearted, invincible and flushed with victory, and they plunged their horses into the swirling river. The weary beasts fought bravely for a moment and then, with their riders, were swept in ever faster circles, until the high waters carried them out to sea. The flood tide of next morning carried their blae bodies ashore beneath the castle wall in full sight of Marian and Mary Craufurd, and the ladies' chamber echoed with their weeping.

The sisters never married after the tragedy but grew old together in the Castle. And so that no other waiting bride or wife or mother would ever again have her life so blighted, they gave their wealth to have a bridge built to loup the river where their lords had perished.

It was the 'new' bridge for a long time but it has been the Auld Brig for much longer and two effigies, that are said to be of Marian and Mary, are rounded, washed smooth and almost undetectable now, on the outside of the most easterly parapet.

Another form of this legend names one of the women as Isabel Lowe, but this contradiction is a detail alongside a more serious question of fact. Records refer to a charter granted for the building of the bridge in 1236 and to its having been raised in the reign of Alexander II, not that of Alexander III, and long before the 1263 Battle of Largs. But the legend persists, so the story may be true, except that the knights' homecoming may have been from a different action.

The Roasting of Allan Stewart

Gilbert Kennedy, 4th Earl of Cassilis, had set his heart on getting the rich and fertile lands of Crossraguel Abbey by Maybole to add to the wide sweep of Carrick country already his by birth. These Crossraguel lands with farms and rich plantations of grain, went with the lay position of being Commendator to the former Benedictine Abbey and that post had recently become available on the death of the last Abbot. (see note)

Gilbert, as the greatest other landowner, thought that his claim to these lands was second to none, as Quintin Kennedy, the last Abbot, had been his uncle. The position of Commendator carried with it rich returns from land, produce and revenues, the farmers who rented ground and property paying him handsomely in bere, horse-corn, capons, muirfowl and salmon. And so Gilbert Kennedy was incensed when a man called Allan Stewart of Kilwinning was appointed to the place that he felt was his by family right. Stewart was a man well into middle age, but one who was reckoned in North Ayrshire to be a figure of influence and power. That such a man would now share Kennedy's previous near monopoly of power in Carrick where in days past he had often been called King Gilbert, filled Kennedy with resentment.

In the early autumn of 1570 Allan Stewart, the 'usurping' Commendator, travelled from Paisley to visit his fat lands at Crossraguel which were golden that year with harvest yield. He was to be the guest of Gilbert Kennedy's kinsman the Laird Bargany who was another power rival in Carrick and who had estates around Ballantrae. While enjoying Bargany's hospitality Allan Stewart took pleasure in visiting the remaining monks at the Abbey, still trying to keep alive the old traditions of fine arts, music and philosophy in an age of dour Reforming zeal. He walked proudly on Crossraguel lands and with perhaps too much satisfaction that all around him there was his.

Meantime Earl Gilbert sulked and schemed in Cassilis Castle bitterly resentful that his rival for the Abbey was being entertained by his rival for the Kingship of Carrick . . . Stewart and Bargany, two thorns in his jealous flesh.

One day while Allan Stewart was walking in the Crossraguel woodlands he was suddenly confronted with an intimidating party of men whose blades and firearms glinted in the mellow sunshine. At their head was Gilbert Kennedy of Cassilis who demanded that Stewart should go back with them to a Kennedy keep on the sea-coast at Dunure, held for him by a small but tough garrison of men. He threw the reins of an unhandsome, riderless horse to Allan Stewart who had little choice but to mount it in the face of the menacing troop with Kennedy.

Dunure Castle sits on an outcrop of rock seven miles from Ayr, the shell of the great stronghold it was then, with its square tower and curtain wall, quite impregnable from the sea, which pounded its foundations. It was difficult of access too from the hill that rose steeply from its front drawbridge. Here Allan Stewart was duly escorted and, with a deep sense of foreboding was thrown into an evil-smelling dungeon. Seeing his rival safely secured in his cell Lord Cassilis went off to the greater comfort of his home at Cassilis.

He gave Stewart a few days to weary of his dungeon, then came back and had him brought up to the main hall. On a table lay a document and writing materials.

37

'If you value your freedom, Allan Stewart, you'll put your name to this deed making over the lands of Crossraguel to me as rightly owns them.'

Doubtless Cassilis thought that in the fluxy state of rivalry between Reformed and Catholic Churches, overlordship of such estates as this one, might legally belong best to the man who had papers saying so. But meantime they were Stewart's by word of the new Kirk (or was it the King's Regent?) and the Commendator did not mean to make them over to the land-hungry Earl of Cassilis. He refused to sign.

The Earl bullied and threatened to no avail and in a fury called his cook, his pantryman and his domestic chaplain to carry Stewart to that part of Dunure Castle called the Black Vault where spitted boars were roasted in times of family residence.

'We'll have a banquet,' called the angry Gilbert. 'Strip the sheep of its fleece!' He pushed Allan Stewart towards the startled domestics who understood that they were to strip the Commendator to his doublet and sark.

'Bind it close the better to roast it,' and the three men bound him hand and foot.

'Fix it on the spit,' and now the servants, warming to the grim joke, threaded the struggling Stewart through his remaining clothes on to the spit and fixed it across the wide fireplace.

'Oil it well with cooking grease that it may brown but not blacken,' cried Cassilis. And the men slapped sheep's fat over the naked flesh and on to the faggots and logs in the grate, the fire whinge'd and smoked a moment and then the flames blazed and licked up round the spit and the hapless victim slung there.

The handle was turned and the flames found every part of Stewart's body.

'Baste it well, cook. Brown it to a crackling,' and the servants poured in more melted fat.

'Will you grace our table, Commendator, or will you stay rare and sign my deed?'

In a torment of pain Stewart cried that he would sign anything. He was taken down and, too agonised to know what he was subscribing, managed to scrawl his name to Lord Cassilis's document, hearing in his dwam that the cook, the pantryman and the chaplain swore an oath on the Bible that they would never reveal to living man what had passed in the Dunure Black Vault. Stewart would be kept meantime, to mend in the Castle. His word of so unlikely a tale could later be denied.

But Gilbert's document had not been properly witnessed by a notary and did not give him even doubtful title to Crossraguel. He came back to Dunure and demanded now of Stewart that, when he was presentable again, he would come with him and sign away the Abbey lands without revealing what had happened previously. But by now the Commendator had regained his spirit and forgotten something of his pain on the spit.

'Do your worst, Gilbert Kennedy. I'd sooner give you my life than another scribing of my name,' he said defiantly.

The servants were called, the fire made ready again and Stewart was laced to the spit. His tender flesh scarcely healed from the last time shrivelled under the flames.

'In God's name despatch me, Cassilis,' he sobbed, as the fire scorched skin and flesh and in places reached his very bones.

'Whing me with your sword, Kennedy, or put powder to me and send me yonder,' screamed Stewart.

'Put an apple to the boar's mouth,' ordered Cassilis, and they stuffed a napkin half-way down his throat to stifle the scream.

'Will you sign?' and the napkin was whipped out again.

'I'll sign.' The sound was barely heard.

'The sheep is done to a turn,' said the King of Carrick with satisfaction.

How great a purse of gold Lord Gilbert had to pay to witness the signing, the Kennedy Historie does not say. But true it is, that Stewart was taken down unconscious, roughly nursed back to enough strength to hold a pen in tortured fingers and sign away his rights to the Crossraguel lands he had thought to enjoy for the rest of his life.

But a pantry scullion had talked and tidings of these dark ill-doings reached Gilbert Kennedy's other rival, the Laird of Bargany at Ballantrae. He had been much put out that Allan Stewart had seemingly left his roof without notice or even a word of thanks and he was now enraged to find out where his guest really was.

With an avenging troop he rode along the banks of the Girvan and sent on a party to see how best to breach the keep at Dunure. It was easy enough to cudgel the gatekeeper and enter, for only the servants were there in charge of the castle and of the near-dead Allan Stewart. Lord Gilbert himself was at Cassilis celebrating the ownership of his new lands when he heard that Bargany's men were holding Dunure. At once, with a hundred men from Maybole, he marched on the keep, but the Bargany men were tightly installed to withstand a small seige. They discharged hagbuts and dropped weighted stones loosened from the battlements and, when they threatened to destroy the castle, Lord Gilbert withdrew his men, only to find that they were surrounded by a Bargany army, furious that their Lord's guest had been used so ill.

Cassilis withdrew and Bargany relieved his besieged men who carried out with them the scorched and twisted form of the Commendator. He was taken safely to Bargany for herb and balm nursing, and haven for the rest of his crippled life.

In due time Earl Gilbert was called to appear before, first the Privy Council and later the Regent and Council but, beyond seeking two thousand pounds from him and cautioning him against further molesting of Allan Stewart, he was not punished. He should by rights have had to face the sterner Court of Justiciary, but these were troubled and violent times for Scotland with their child King, and the Regent's party may have thought it discreet to have the powerful Cassilis as their friend rather than their enemy. For the time being too, Bargany sheathed his sword and the lairds of Scotland closed ranks in truce to put their strength behind their young King.

It may have been that ordinary local folk were so incensed by the leniency meted out to the cruel Earl of Cassilis that wishful myths grew up around him, the final and most lasting ones concerning sightings at the time of his death.

They do say that six years after the roasting of the Commendator the master of an Irish coaster sailing down the Firth of Clyde, in the lee of Ailsa Craig, saw coming towards him across the water a chariot and horses wreathed in fire. The master shouted to the spirit driver,

'Whence and whither are you bound?'

'From Hell to Cassilis for the soul of Earl Gilbert Kennedy,' called back the driver.

Then the master saw the chariot of fire returning from land with a passenger at his side.

Next day the sailor heard that Lord Gilbert had been thrown from his horse and fatally injured the day before.

And there were those who told that at the funeral a great black crow had cruised about the death carriage and landed once or twice on the coffin. Each time the bird alighted the horses stopped and would not move on until the omen bird spread its wings and circled the procession again.

Much tradition and superstition surrounds this story yet there is incontrovertible evidence that the history of the 'roasting' was nothing but the nasty truth. In the *Historie of the Kennedys* the account is quaintly titled 'The Erle Cassilis' Tyranny against a Quick Man' and reports that Allan Stewart showed his disfigured body publicly at Ayr mercat cross.

Commendators: At this Reformation period the old Church laws of land tenure were giving way to the laws of the new Kirk and, as heads of religious houses (such as Crossraguel Abbey) died or were ousted, notable laymen were appointed to manage such communities until the new Reformed arrangements came into operation. These were the Commendators and part of their reward was the income they would have meantime from the Ecclesiastical estates. Allan Stewart was one of the men thus appointed.

The Breaking of the Sabbath

In the village of Ochiltree at the top of the street Mr. *Thomas* Smith the blacksmith was sitting having his Sunday afternoon nap having attended the morning diet of worship at the kirk, while at the bottom of the street, Mr. *John* Smith, the minister, was at the same time putting the numbers one, two and three to the headings of his sermon that Thomas would hear at that evening's service.

Along towards the hamlet around three o'clock came a horseman leading by the bridle a limping horse with a nail which had been badly placed that week by another blacksmith ten miles away. The nail was stabbing the hoof and the animal was in great pain. The man who led him was a doctor called to a woman in childbed and enquiries of a gudewife walking in her garden at the outskirts of the village directed him to Thomas's smiddy on the brae. He chapped the door and the smith lumbered through the lobby to open it. They conversed a moment or two at the door-slab and Thomas inspected the horse. His smithing was something of a calling and he had never been able to bear the sight of an animal in distress and pain, so his hesitation lasted barely a moment. His nod had in it the queer suggestion of a shake of the head.

'There'll be a reckoning, mind, this being the Sabbath, but I cannae see your mare leave my place hirpling.'

A rise of sparks from Sunday embers, a resounding clang that wakened every busybody in Ochiltree, and the cruel nail was out. A firm comfortable shoe sat snug on the hoof and the grateful rider was off on his errand of mercy. And in the time it took him to be at the end of the village a shocked and godly parish worthy was dutifully, and, of course reluctantly, stammering out his clipe to the minister.

The good Reverend John Smith had an hour on his knees, for he was sore flummoxed. Thomas Smith had done no different from what he himself might have done had he been a blacksmith. But, be that as it may, the man had broken the Sabbath and given a wee edge for other backsliders, with less good reason, to unhallow the day of rest.

'And if Thomas Smith was the minister over me he might just have to act as stern wi' me as I mean to be with him and forbid me my Communion token for my sin,' said the minister to his lady-wife.

The Kirk was more the law than was the Laird, in Ochiltree, as it was in other parishes, and in due course Thomas Smith was reprimanded by the Ochiltree Session and denied a place at the Lord's Supper for some time to come. But dour authority or no, the lower Kirk courts could be challenged if a common man, examined, felt that he had been wronged.

43

Thomas Smith was a godly layman and thought honestly that he had done right, acting only in Christian compassion for the mare. And he knew his Kirk.

He had no need to submit, cowed, to the Session, and maybe John Smith himself secretly applauded him for taking his case to the next court up, to the Presbytery. That body in its turn upheld the Session. Still not satisfied, Thomas approached the third court, the Synod. But the Synod too, saw the Sabbath horse-shoeing as sin. The blacksmith had but one more appeal to make … a last recourse away almost beyond his ken, to the great General Assembly itself, in Edinburgh.

Men and women who had never ventured much beyond Catrine and could scarcely imagine a place bigger than Cumnock, gathered at the Ochiltree Cross or in knots about the village to crack over the rights and wrongs of the matter and to wonder at the great case the smith had sent to be chawed over in Edinburgh. There were those who saw the cliper as doing only his duty and others who thought he would have been better employed smoking his pipe and ignoring the ringing echoes from the anvil. But the controversy now that it had come, was meat and drink to disputatious Scots Kirkmen.

In the end honour was sorted out. Thomas Smith won his appeal and took the Lord's Supper among the rest of the congregation and, truth to tell, John Smith was glad of it, for he was not a vindictive man but nevertheless one anxious to see his flock living in righteous obedience to the Word. And Thomas bore no ill-will to the minister who had only done in *his* calling exactly what Thomas had done in his.

The village went back to its sleepy routine. And maybe none among its inhabitants thought from its recent experience that they lived in a society where, though there was much amiss with it, there were also hard-won rights for common men and women that were worth preserving. And yet, at least *one* must have thought so or else this story would not have been passed down through the generations to be remembered now.

The government of the Scottish Church is by courts of Elders (Greek-presbus, old; presbuteros, older). These courts range upwards from the Kirk Sessions of individual congregations through district Presbyteries and area Synods, to the national court, the General Assembly. Thomas Smith was exercising his rights as a normally communicant member of the Kirk in appealing successively to these courts and the incident was something of a *cause célèbre* in Ochiltree.

The Curse on 'The Gift of God'

The elders of Irvine Kirk Session sat solemnly down the sides of the long session-room like so many black crows. Those who knew the men as individuals were aware that this one in his personal life was generous and kindly, that one pawky and jovial and another hard and shrewd, all as different from one another as fisher and farmer. But as a body of brethren they were narrow and strict to a man, ready to punish and humiliate any who appeared before them and were found guilty of sin.

It was a summer evening of 1618 and the court had been in session for an hour. They had questioned and scolded into wedlock a pair who had meddled with each other in the spring. They had also sentenced to sackcloth and cutty, a persistent hooligan and a bardy lad who had gone poaching on the Sabbath.

And now they awaited a foursome accused of an even more serious crime; they adjusted their minds and neckcloths in readiness and coughed with nervous anticipation. They all knew the story so far and perhaps in more detail than the good citizens of Irvine, who had added fiction to rumour and secret, so that the whole town was agog with the scandal.

Some months before that evening, the brothers Archibald and John Dean were dining together with their wives Margaret and Janet. The two couples were not always on the best of terms and during the evening an argument over some triviality flared up and tempers became tattered. Jibe followed jibe and snipe answered snipe. A climax came when Janet Dean accused Margaret Dean of having been guilty in the past of some unspecified act of theft.

Tradition does not tell how the evening itself ended, but the accusation rankled sorely in Margaret Dean and she decided to raise an accusation of slander against her sister-in-law before the Kirk Session.

Tiffs and quarrels among the comfortably respectable members of the congregation brought discredit on the Kirk and were a poor example to lesser mortals, and so the Irvine session tried to pacify the two women privately. They ordered a reconciling handshake which Margaret at least gave with exceedingly listless fingers.

'I give you my hand, Janet Dean, only in obeydence to the

45

minister there, for I cannae forget the name you cried me and got the whole toon believing it.'

If Margaret had not raised her action the 'whole toon' might have remained totally ignorant of the incident. As it was she had laid the first faggot on a fire that would soon rage in the sight of everyone. In spite of the handshake, she nursed hatred and ill will for Janet Dean, and soon all Irvine was taking sides.

Margaret had at least the half-hearted support of her burgess husband. John Dean, Janet's man, was the skipper of the vessel 'Gift of God' and away for long periods at sea. Some weeks after the Session compearance he set sail in the 'Gift' for France. One of his passengers was Provost Andrew Tran who was part-owner of the ship's cargo on that voyage.

Perhaps Margaret was on the quay buying fish or simply taking a turn by the sea in the spring sunshine with her friends Isabel Craufurd and Isobel Insh, and was perhaps heard mumbling ill things against the 'Gift of God' and those on board. Whatever the mutterings were, someone claimed to have heard and remembered them.

Some time later word came back that the ship had gone down off the English coast at Padstow. Suspicion fed on the news since it reached Irvine, not by ordinary channels, but with a ne'er do weel vagabond in the town known as John Stewart, who had been wandering in the south and had heard there of the sinking. This tale was confirmed when two surviving sailors from the ship made their way home to Irvine and told their tale.

Pure accident in high seas or faulty seamanship were not tidy enough reasons among the Irvine folk for the loss of good menfolk, one of them their First Citizen. They looked round superstitiously for better ones and, doubtless with Janet Dean to point the finger, found them in Margaret Dean's dogged dislike for her in-laws. Clash rippled round Irvine. Word of it came to Kirk Session ears and by the time Margaret Barclay Dean was sent for, to face their charge, her friends Isabel and Isobel were implicated with her and so was the hapless vagabond, John Stewart. And a formidable charge it was.

Whatever those mutterings of Margaret's had been the day the 'Gift of God' sailed, they were now set forth officially as having been a wicked curse and death wish on its crew and passengers. The prosecution case was that, after laying it, she had consulted, some-how and somewhere, with John Stewart (thought to be an expert in

46

the black arts): that in company with Satan, disguised in the form of a black lap-dog, she had moulded clay figures of the ship's crew, and a fair-headed one to represent Provost Tran; and that they had gone down to the wharf at dead of night and thrown these in the water. By all these means and with deliberate intent they had caused the foundering of 'Gift of God' and the deaths by drowning of all but a few survivors.

The evidence was given and sifted, the accused questioned, all was considered and pondered, over several diets of the Kirk Session and, in the godly wisdom of the day, the elders found that the charges were fully proven. There was a verdict of 'Guilty' and all that remained was to wrest confession for the sake of their souls from the murdering sinners. An appeal for confession fell on deaf ears at first, for all four indignantly and fearfully protested their innocence. But the use of weights to torture their limbs eventually drew out of their agonised bodies admission of their guilt as witches and warlock, and the elders were satisfied.

There was only one possible sentence to root out sin and witchcraft from a Christian community. It was pronounced that four stakes would be set up for the guilty. The wandering beggar, John Stewart and Isobel Insh jouked the public gibbet, Stewart by hanging himself in his cell and the woman by the fatal injuries sustained when she fell from the Kirk roof in a frenzied effort to escape from the high belfry (though folklore does not tell how she managed to find her way there).

Margaret Barclay Dean was taken out to face her execution and declared in terror before the crowd,

'All I have confessed was in agony of torture and, before God, I declare now that the confessing was false and untrue.' Then she is said to have calmed down when she saw her shamefaced burgess husband Archibald Dean for the first time since her trouble began. Her gaze swept over him scornfully.

'You have been too long coming, husband,' she said with great bitterness, before she was pushed towards the place of execution.

Then she and Isabel Craufurd were strangled at their stakes before a huge mob. Their slumped bodies were tarred, the piles of faggots round their feet were lit and the whole ghastly spectacle of human figures consumed in bonfire served once again to remind ordinary folk to keep close guard on too quick tongues for fear of ever sharing the same fate.

In his book *The Burgh of Irvine* Arnold F. McJannet refers to the Scottish Act against Witchcraft of 1563. One can see from that date, so soon after the Reformation was established, that the new Kirk set out very early to put an end to witchcraft. There were subsequent alternating periods of leniency and persecution but around 1698 there was a great upsurge of determined witch-hunting. The first examination of a suspect through to acquittal, or more often conviction, followed a pattern:

a. Repeated examination by Session and Presbytery.
b. The setting up of a witch council to take evidence from neighbours and acquaintances.
c. Trial by ordeal; by floating or sinking in water, by length of resistance to unendurably heavy weights laid on the body, by use of a witch-pin.
d. Then, if guilty, the accused was strangled, covered with pitch and burned publicly at the stake.

48

Blind Harry's Tale of
William Wallace

The lad, William, was a steering handful to his noble family, the Wallaces of Elderslie, and they thought to channel some of his roaring energies constructively by putting him to a priest in Dunipace for tutoring. But the man was not only a scholar, he was a fervid patriot as well. And so in this 13th Century Scotland which had become a sovereign power under the great King Alexander III with his Golden Age, Wallace grew up into his teens with a passionate sense of his country's nationhood, and a temper that made wise people, who had any sort of disagreement with him, skirt his path.

And then Scotland was thrown into confusion and division, by the tragic accident that pitched Alexander from his horse over a Kinghorn cliff, and by the death of his heir, the little Maid of Norway. Scotland was now prey to England. The land was quickly conquered by Edward I, The Hammer of the Scots, and once again lay dominated by a foreign power.

Wallace, like many another, bitterly resented the occupying armies and his anger smouldered. Simply being English seems to have been enough to merit a blow from his staff or blade and his first recorded quarrel was with an English soldier, one of those the minstrels of the time called 'Southrons'. They exchanged angry words, then blows and finally William drew his dagger and stabbed the man to death.

He fled the east coast and reached Ayrshire, an unrepentant young man wanted for his crime. In Ayrshire he was shuffled among his kinfolk who had lands there, none keeping him too long for fear of retribution against them from the English King who was their overlord. They would have had Wallace hide himself away, for the present at least, from vengeful authority, but the young man had no intention of being contained and strode openly about town and countryside pursuing his pleasures as he pleased.

The second feat of coolness and strength which men came to sing about in later years is said to have erupted when Wallace was fishing quietly in the River Irvine in the spring of 1297 with a small boy from his present lodgings. They sat by a clump of thorn, known since as the Bickering Bush, and during the afternoon Lord Percy of the English army rode by with a small troop of his green-clad men.

Tradition says that five of them hung back, after Percy and the main troop had passed on, and that they demanded what fish the two had already caught. A steely glimmer came into William's eye but, minding the child's safety, politely offered them half. One of the troopers dismounted and calmly took all the fish lying at the boy's feet and stowed them into his own knapsack.

Wallace held out a steady hand for their return.

'Leave us some, I pray you, for an aged knight we know, who lives nearby,' he said with an edge to his voice now.

'I think *my* lord shall have these fishes for his supper,' said Percy's man. 'There are plenty more in the river waiting for your worm.'

Once more Wallace protested and now he sent the child out of harm's way. The soldier drew his foolish sword but Wallace lifted his staff and felled him before the blade was even raised. The man dropped the sword to William who now had staff in one hand and sword in the other. The remaining four green-tunics made to jump down and two were slain before their feet touched the ground, the fifth had picked up the fish-satchel but dropped it again as he fled.

Lord Percy judged his knights so craven that he did not even avenge them but thoughtfully marked out this giant fisherman as a man to be watched.

Wallace's kinfolk, and especially his uncle Sir Ranald Craufurd, were concerned, now that they saw what manner of wight this nephew was, to keep his strength out of danger, against the day when it might be needed in an organised rising against the English. They supplied him with life's necessities but gave him no more than a few nights' hospitality at a time, so that he would not be easily surprised. And so William wandered the wooded countryside with its rocky burns, sheltering caves and riverside recesses, and sometimes spent a night on a chaff in a friendly cot house. From time to time, legend tells, he made forays into town and village and felled unwary or arrogant occupying soldiers, with alarming ease and insolence. In an Ayr, swarming with troops, he met a giant Southron, who stood at the Mercat Cross and bawled out his boast that for a wager of one shilling he would take on anyone. Wallace accepted his challenge and delivered him such a blow that the man is said to have spun round thrice before he fell dead in a crumpled heap. The braggart's companions made at Wallace, but the ballads say that he cut a swathe through them as if they were ripe corn, slaying another half dozen as he went.

Tales of his prowess multiplied. There was another version of the stealing of the fish, and there was the rousing story of a confrontation with a multitude of bullying Percy soldiers who taunted him from the safety of their numbers massing on the street, and of Wallace hewing them down like a flock of silly sheep. And there was the telling of how he was finally overcome from behind, carried off to prison, fell ill from tainted herring and, thought to be dead, was thrown over the castle wall. There he was found by his old nurse who cosseted him back to vengeful health.

His reputation in the South-West was now enormous and his followers grew in numbers to match. His armed force was strong enough to face its first battle and to intercept supplies bound for the Ayr garrison from Carlisle. They assembled on Mauchline Moor, marched on Loudon Hill, won the day and seized the vittling supplies. Another single combat incident, this time against a challenger at Ayr town gate, ended in Wallace cutting his way through a tumult of reinforcement. There was fury in the garrison and Wallace fled to Lanark.

Up till this time William is reckoned only to have been proving his mettle in a series of displays of fiery temper and great strength, but it was here in Lanark that tradition and Blind Harry claim he struck the first real, calculated blow for Scottish independence.

The old gentlewoman who sheltered him in Lanark was slain for her pains after he left the town. Cold and furious with distaste for the English overlordship he came back, sought out Hesilrig, the English Sheriff and killed him. Then he roused the whole town to his side; they routed the troops and pronounced English rule at an end there.

During the weeks following there were skirmishes and encounters with parties of Edward's soldiers, Wallace drew more supporters and he and other leaders of Scottish rebels were ordered to appear at a Court of Justiciary at the Barns of Ayr, once the Town granary and now the English garrison.

By now proud lairds all over the country were chafing under the shame of calling Edward their king and tired of living under floundering leadership and power struggle. Nowhere were they more restless than in Ayrshire. Now Wallace had fanned up the kindling and his uncle Sir Ranald Craufurd with his friends sensed that time was ripening for a rebellion. A plan was made for a meeting (just before the due hearing at the Court in the Barns of Ayr) of these lairds and gentlemen, to choose a leader who might draw the factions together and inspire a great army to drive the English back over the Border. The matter was heavy on their hearts and it was a sober band who gathered that day in a corner of the church at Monkton.

The analysing and planning went on for hours and then at last they elected one of their number to be their undoubted leader. They gave him a high-sounding national title and position, prematurely bestowed no doubt, but certainly in keeping with their lofty aspirations.

'Warden of Scotland' was what they dubbed William Wallace that day; Wallace of the prodigious and legendary warrior strength, the man who was to lead his vassal country to independence.

Now the meeting was over, the 'kingmakers' and campaigners slipped away quietly and singly from the church not to be kenspeckle to any English soldiers who might be out on reconnaissance duty.

Blind Harry's song now weaves its tradition through the barer records and tells that William lingered by the church after the others left and went into the chapel itself to say a Pater Noster and a creed, and to pray for guidance and strength in the task his uncle's friends had put on him. Passionately he laid his needs before God and sat afterwards in such deep meditation that sleep overcame him and he put his head wearily against the stone. And he dreamed Blind Harry's Dream.

He dreamed that a stalwart man came and stood before him, drawing forward his hands and laying across them a sword of finest steel with a pommel of topaz, its hilt and studdings glittering with jewels.

'Thou must avenge thy country's wrongs,' declared the messenger, and led him through the haar of his dream to the high reaches of a great mountain, where he left him alone.

From this place Wallace could look down on the whole land from Ross in the North, to the Solway, all of it wasting in fire. And then out of the misty edges of the vision appeared a beautiful queen so dazzling that the fire around him seemed to dim. She gave him a green and scarlet wand and crossed his head with a sapphire.

'You must help the poor and the oppressed. But first you must go to the house of your uncle, Sir Ranald Craufurd, and make plans there to redeem your kingdom.' And before she ascended into the clouds she gave him a book. It was set out in three parts: in the first the letters were of brass, in the second of pure gold and in the third of finest silver.

In his dream he began to read ... but the cold of the stone floor chilled him through his sleeping and he shivered as he wakened in the church. But the vision was as sharp as the dagger at his belt as he made his way across the moor to Sir Ranald at Crocebie.

On the way, as if it was a part still trailing from his trance, he met an old seer, a venerable wandering holy man from an abbey to the north, who interpreted his dream for him.

'The stalwart man of your vision was Fergus, long ago the King of Scots. The mountain is The Hill of Knowledge of Wrongs. The fire is Hasty Tidings for urgent action. The Queen is Fortune, a portent of the good task you are to do. The wand is Power and Command, red for blood, green for courage. The sapphire blessing is Happy Chance. The book is the Land of Scotland, brass foretelling War for Independence, gold for Honour and True Worth, and silver for Heavenly Bliss after a clean life.'

Then the seer blessed William Wallace, who thanked the old man and went his way to Crocebie. He lodged there quietly and made his plans.

It was decided that first they must make their appearance at the Court of Justiciary at the Barns of Ayr. There they would take the opportunity to declare their defiance of English rule, though chivalry would demand that no blood be shed on that occasion, for they would be carrying a Charter of Peace and Safe Conduct from Edward to the meeting.

On this expedition Wallace and his uncle set off from Crocebie and halfway along the journey realised that they had left their safe-conduct letter at Sir Ranald's home. Wallace went back to collect it while the rest of the party went on, thinking that the spirit of the charter would be honoured until it arrived.

But the whole meeting was a trap, with or without the document of peace. As each of the lairds who had been compeired to face the court, stepped from bright day into the gloom of the garrison, he was seized, then strangled and bundled away to be hanged from the Barn wall. Sir Bryce Blair, Sir Neil Montgomery, Kennedys, Campbells, Barclays, Boyds and Stewards and finally Sir Ranald Craufurd himself, all died by treachery that day.

Wallace was on his way too now and heard of the slaughter from a woman who did washing at the Barns and was fleeing from the dreadful sight. The old Wallace might have burst into the garrison swirling his great sword, and laid about him but 'The Warden of Scotland' diverted to the Laglane Woods, where he had done much of his own hiding and his gathering of support. There he assembled his troop and marched to the Barns, breaking order half a mile away and stealing in quietly on the building from all sides. Inside there was wine and wassail, celebrating the culling of Scottish leadership and none was aware that outside torches were being set to the base of the walls all around them. The entire complex of buildings was burned down and all those inside died, smothered, burned, or trampled in the frenzy.

And the gutting of the Barns did not finish the day of vengeance, for the Prior of Ayr and his seven brothers, outraged at the lack of honourable chivalry over the safe-conducts, swept round the other places in Ayr where the soldiery was lodged and put them to the fire or drove them to drown in the Friars' Well. This Christlike event went down in minstrelsy as The Blessing of Ayr.

They say that after the firing of the Barns of Ayr Wallace rode to the top of a nearby slope to admire his handiwork and remarked with satisfaction to a companion,

'Aye, the Barns burn weel, friend, the Barns burn weel,'
(and the incident has ever since been remembered in tradition and in the Ayrshire name Barnweil).

And then Wallace turned his horse and rode with a troop to Ardrossan. This time they set fire to part of the out-buildings and waited to pounce on the 'Southrons' as they came out to extinguish the flames. The Scots set upon them, killed the party, then forced the castle and threw the slain into the food-store cellars, afterwards known grimly as Wallace's Larder.

Ayrshire was now in a ferment, and the stage was set for a general uprising in Scotland. And so the lore of Wallace in the South-West ends. The marching across Scotland, the laying of siege to keeps and castles, the great victory at Stirling Bridge, the final capture, trial, hanging drawing and quartering for his manifest seditions, the eventual re-establishing of Scotland as a sovereign country, all these belong to the national story.

But Ayrshire claims his early days, the first evidence of his powers of leadership, his skill and prowess as a warrior in the violent and

54

bloodthirsty times when these were the qualities that made a man a man.

These legends concerning William Wallace's days in Ayrshire, have as their source the narrative epic *The Life of the Noble Champion of Scotland* by Henry the Minstrel (Blind Harry) one of the great war poets of medieval times.

The Barnweil tradition of this story is highly suspect as fact. There is firstly a ring of untruth about the 700 year-old pun, and secondly there is a more likely origin suggested by various more recent authorities in the Celtic name 'Bar-n-wyld' (Hill of Streams), known in Ayrshire since ancient times.

Jock Neill, the Coals Carter

Every day Jock Neill drove coals from Newbiggin heuches to Irvine harbour. He was a queer-shaped man with a lanky body and a pair of bow-hurdied legs on him. When he wasn't driving, he loped alongside his horse with a shuffle to his feet and a slouch to his shoulders that made folk think he might just have slaked his thirst at the alehouse, even though the truth was he seldom touched a drop. He wore an ancient bonnet too, pulled down over straggling black hair, and a grey coat that had seen much better days flapped now round ill-fitting boots. But Jock had a glint in his eye and a clench to his jaw and when he slid the grey coat down off his shoulders, shed his boots and slapped his bonnet on the green or over a rock on a firm stretch of sand, well, it was a different Jock the parish knew then.

He was skliffing alongside his old horse making towards Irvine one early spring morning when he was in his hearty young days, his collar up, frayed trousers trailing through puddles, his bonnet pulled down against a smir of rain. He heard the clop of hooves some distance behind him and when he saw the horse gaining on him he began to move towards the hedgerow to leave the hurrying rider space to pass. He was not quite fast enough, however, to suit the horseman who reined in quickly, swore an oath, called Jock a 'cannibal' and flicked his whip smartly across the carter's grey unshaven cheek. Neill caught a glimpse of ruddy fresh skin, cold slate-blue eyes and closely cropped ginger hair, before the stranger's spurs drew a spatter of blood from his animal and he disappeared in a cloud of dust round a bend in the track.

On the evening of that same day, the Earl of Eglinton was giving dinner to a party of officers from the English Cavalry lying in Irvine and the talk turned to a young officer of their company whose fame as a matchless runner and jumper was known to a dozen other regiments of the King's Army. He practised every day, said the officers, against challenge times kept by his fellows of the Irvine station.

'They don't do it for great love of the man, for he's a cold fellow ... a good soldier though ... and there isn't one among us who isn't in awe of his prowess, I promise you,' said his Colonel to Lord Eglinton.

'A race against another man would surely give a better sporting contest, would it not?' suggested Eglinton.

'Certainly if one could match him . . . but none can.' The Colonel shrugged and the Earl lifted his decanter.

'I think we might have one hereabouts to test him.'

'Never! Impossible! Waste of time!' Half a dozen sallies and plain laughter greeted his suggestion. Eglinton smiled.

'Will you wager, gentlemen?'

There was an almost unseemly haste to lay bets.

The course was set from Townhead Toll in Irvine to the Red Burn, six miles back and forth, and both men agreed separately to run the contest . . . Eglinton's challenger and the Cavalry champion.

Within the week the day came. Jock carted his coals as usual in the morning, leading Maggie without harsh word or haste. He delivered them to the harbour and calmly stabled the horse, and all through his steady routine he himself chewed away stolidly at horse-beans. Then he made his way, slouching along to the Town End to join the crowd of men already gathered there. At one side was an attendant knot of spanking smart soldiers preparing their hero, whose snow-white pantaloons were tight and perfect across the bottom, which was then facing Jock. Then the man straightened up and turned round.

Something near excitement spread into every muscle of Jock's unlikely body, for it was Fresh Face with the ginger hair who was to run the race. The blue eyes regarded the carter coolly at first, then with amazement, when he realized that this was his opponent. And then amusement took over and filled the ruddy face when Jock began to shed his greatcoat, his jacket and his waistcoat, and shook them to the ground. Then he added his boots and stockings to the pile and stood there, a braw, funny sight in his short sark and nankeen breeks, the coal dust still on his hands.

'It's never the Cannibal!' And the ginger-headed cavalryman shook with mirth and was for dressing himself up again and going home.

But those who had wagered would have none of that and so he shrugged and laughed and took up his place alongside Jock, but not too close to him. He wore a silken singlet, a pair of red Morocco slippers and silk hose, and he moved as supple as an eel.

When the signal came, the Englishman shot off like an arrow from

57

a bow, moving like a gull, beautiful to watch and, on the first lap, far
ahead of the shauchling carter with the ham thighs. Indeed Jock met
the man on his way back from the touching post where the army
supporters spluttered with greedy mirth. Jock heard the impudent
officer fling a word or two over his shoulder.

'You run like you were pulling your own cart Cannibal!'

But Jock was on the turn now and, stung by the scornful soldier,
he simply put his great head down. Thoroughly limbered up, he
found the ground running faster under his bare feet with every lap
while the soldier, still moving sweet as honey, slackened pace on the
third turn out. Then they were shoulder to shoulder, and bare foot to
red slipper, and Jock was scarcely panting. He took time even to
steep his burning feet a moment in the stream on his next lap. And
then he galloped home.

'Five hundred yards,' the parish lads said he was in front at the end.
'Two hundred,' said the watching soldiers. But the seconds knew the
right of it and called it 'Three hundred'. Jock touched the fading
mark of the whip-lash on his cheek and felt that revenge was sweet.
He would even have shaken that young upstart's hand if his own had
not been so grimed.

'You run well, Cannibal, and they tell me you jump a man's height
too. I think I'll not contest that with you.'

The soldiers saw him take the carter's paw and pump it, and it was
a queer thing that they gave their man a heartier cheer this time when
he lost, than they had ever given him before, when he had triumphed.

White-Pantaloons was not lodged at Irvine long after that, but
before he left, the few times that he met Jock Neill on the road
walking at his horse's head, he did not stop, but he did salute the
carter and call out a brisk 'Good Morning'.

The Smuggling Coultarts

In the days when old Rob Forgie, with his scarlet night-cap and his swelling girth, kept the ale-house by Bennane Craig, he was not only host and landlord but also the watchman who fluttered a white warning sheet in the daylight, or set fire to a gorse-bush by night, if any of the gauger men were to be seen when a landing of illicit goods was due.

Among his customers he had old men with long memories who sat a whole evening at the one filling of ale, and callow youths he had to warn about taking too many, but his favourite clients were the seven huge Coultart brothers, wild, reckless and free-spending. He didn't always know which was which, for in appearance and style they were all much of a muchness and only Hewie Coultart was kenspeckle for being the eldest, the leader and the tallest by half a head.

They worked their bit of land with reasonable efficiency but would down tools at the drop of a bonnet if there were smuggled goods to be received and run inland.

One night after a successful run and stowing away of their tax-jouked cargo the brothers were sitting in Rab's howff in comfortable satisfaction over their profitable day, and relaxing themselves with heedless freedom round a table littered with their illicit drinks. Rab, tempted away from his watch-post, had joined them in their celebration and was as taken aback as any when the house was surrounded by a body of thirteen excisemen who called out loudly for the surrender of the seven.

'Surrender' was not a word the Coultarts understood and even in their dwam they were not so fuddled that they couldn't plan their strategy to outwit the gaugers. They gave Rab another mouthful of spirit courage and then sent him out as go-between with their defiant message to the officers.

'If you want them Coultarts, you maun come in and carry them oot, for they cannae stand, never mind walk oot to you.'

The massive Hewie Coultart signed to his brothers to lie or crouch in a row making a path of bodies into the room from the door (leaving just enough space for it to open). Then he himself doused the tallows, grabbed a baking griddle from the swee as a targe-shield and a brandy bottle as a cudgel.

Rab had been thrown aside and then the door was splintered and kicked open. One by one the Captain's men stumbled over the six bodies and, as they struggled to rise, were either caught round the ankles by the great Coultart hands or felled again by an ungentle tap from Hewie's brandy bottle. The Captain had hung back to command the seizure and, as he was last to need clubbing, Hew backed now and, standing over the sprawl of gaugers hurled the bottle straight at his head and brought him down as sweet and clean as a skittle.

Thirteen brave excisemen lay about the floor, bloodied but in no danger of their lives. The brothers mopped up and salved the gaugers' bruises and then steadied their spinning heads with brandy ... which cure they found so efficacious that they repeated and increased the dose until they were as stunned with the inside contents of the bottle as they had previously been with the outside.

Next day Hewie Coultart dictated a note for Rab to send back with the crestfallen excisemen to their commanding officer, thanking him for the visit of his men and stating that they had been given a night's lodging and hospitality and been treated to a bottle apiece.

60

Checkmate

'Checkmate, Milord,' said Matthew Hay, as he smiled with satisfaction and moved his knight to finish the chess game, much to the chagrin of his opponent, Henry Home. Henry Home was Lord Kames, one of the Scottish Law Lords presently on circuit in southwest Scotland and whiling away an evening of early spring 1780 with this somewhat socially ambitious acquaintance of his friend, Sir William Cuningham of Caprintoun.

Hay leaned back and tucked his fingers expansively into his waistcoat pocket, proud as much of the company he was keeping as of his skill with the pieces. To the surprise of some to whom he was a stranger, he called for drinks for all at present in the dining-room of the hostelry in Ayr and paid for them before he left with notes apparently issued by the currently fashionable local banking company of Douglas and Heron.

Matthew Hay of Holms farm Dundonald, was a well-to-do robust and handsome man, reckoned in all of five parishes to be an innovative, progressive and well-organised tenant farmer on the Eglinton estate, and highly regarded by the Earl himself. There was no doubt in local minds that of almost equal return to him as the farming was the smuggling which was now so rife along the Ayrshire coast. But as Matthew Hay rode home that night, he reflected complacently that if that was the only stain on his reputation, he could live with it fairly comfortably and continue his upward progress into the gentry circles of Ayrshire with men like Cuningham, and even into the gentry of Edinburgh ... for was he not now quite far ben with the likes of Kames and his colleague the fierce Lord Braxfield who did not intimidate him in the least in these days of his prosperity? And fortune had begun to smile even more brightly on Matthew's ambitions these past weeks, for Sir William Cuningham had taken a fancy to his bonnie sister, Mary Hay as-was-now and Lady Cuningham to-be, if he could play his hand right and steer the two into marriage.

61

As well as the smuggling, Hay had several other dubious pursuits that he preferred to keep much more closely secret, but for the present, and perhaps for ever, these seemed very unlikely to come to light.

He had, of course, so many activities to steer that he was never without the superficial concern of any administrator or employer, but these were, in general, only an interesting challenge to him. The smuggling trade was one. He thought now of its wildfire spread all the way along the coast and that its general respectability made for increasing safety for those who took part. But it was also becoming bigger business, needing steady financing at this stage to establish it properly and to buy the large amounts of tea and brandy that made it all a worthwhile enterprise. He was a leader in the organising and men looked to him for money. But his capital had been tied up always in his farm and that he could not risk. He smiled in the darkness as he rode through Symington, thinking of the astute way he had solved that problem and wondered how much more it could be milked. He had made contacts in France in the early excise-dabbling days and had found a printer and engraver in Dunquerque who was happy to oblige his friend, M. Matthieu by making fac-similes of Douglas and Heron Bank notes, for a small return. Now the bills were circulating all over Ayrshire, and Matthieu whipped up his mare, threw back his head and laughed in the face of the wind at the thought of having paid for the Judges' drinks with forged notes from France. He galloped exultantly along the road to Holms, the finest house in the parish, fit for any gentry as might call, with its two storeys and its high handsome windows, his checked plaid streaming out behind him.

It was late when he finally went upstairs, took his nightly look out through the small gable window from which he could watch for luggers coming in towards Troon and then turned into the bed-chamber where his wife was already asleep. Through the years she had seemed to remain in comfortable ignorance of his activities and he sometimes thought that a more intelligent woman would have suspected the source of her comforts. Maybe however (for she had not been a stupid girl when he married her) she suspected it well-enough, but found it more convenient to enjoy them with an uninformed conscience. He was fond enough of Mistress Hay but as he slipped under the covers beside her he thought with more pleasure of the dark eyes, the rosy cheeks and the buxom form of the lass he would be holding in his arms the following night in Ploughlands farm barn.

He played another game of chess that next evening with Lord Kames before he stopped by at Ploughlands. He was tenant of the small, poor-soiled croft as well as of Holms, and Lizzie Wilson's father ran it for him as his grieve. But tonight his tryst was in the barn where Lizzie met him. He had his way with her, as he had had it for near two months and he lay back in the hay afterwards looking up through the open top-half of the door at the clear night sky and thinking himself a clever and lusty fellow to have two such pleasures on the same night.

But Lizzie had a denting in store for his self-satisfaction and she delivered it now as she sat there smoothing down her tumbled clothes.

'You'll have to see me right wi' a bit siller, Master Hay,' she said in a matter-of-fact voice.

Alarm bells rang somewhere in the distance of Matthew's dark conscience. And they were not particularly on account of the money itself, for any amount that Lizzie could contemplate would be easily enough found.

'Siller?' he said warily.

'Aye, I'm wi' bairn.'

'To me?'

For answer she looked up from blazing eyes and slapped his face. Hard. And there was no doubt that there was honest indignation in the slap, though in truth it could have been delivered but to underline her demand.

'When?' he asked. The further away the better.

'Near Candlemas. Before, like enough.'

Hay closed his eyes on this information and digested it silently. Lizzie Wilson must go away to have this child, for a whole handful of reasons.

'I'll give you siller to go away to Edinburgh to bide there till it's your time, and maybe after. Fifty pounds I'll give you, and some-a-year for all your life. I can maybe find you a place there forbye.'

Lizzie sensed his agitation and was shrewd enough to realise that he was offering her far more than she was asking, more than he had given Janet Jack in the same plight. She guessed that she might have even more to come from Master Hay if she stayed in Dundonald and squeezed his pouch from time to time through the next few months. Besides she knew no one in Edinburgh. He certainly seemed more bothered about her condition than she would have expected him to be. After all ... master and maid ... it was a common enough situation. But maybe he wanted to keep it from his wife. She looked at him coyly.

'No, I think I'll just bide here. You'll can give me a wee purse whiles, maybe some of them notes you was so proud to show me a while back', said Lizzie, and Hay cursed the memory of the day he had boasted to her of that, thinking her too ignorant to understand. Now he knew perfectly well that she was capable of bruiting, not only her own situation, but rumours of the forging story all over the parish and beyond.

He was a serious man that night as he walked down to Holms. There had been a time when he would have gloried in his reputation as a hard-living man who could have his pick of the parish lasses and who could sail so close to the wind in many of his doings and still keep out of the hands of the law. But that day was past. It was certainly not his first marital transgression. But he did not want his wife to know about this one, for she had been coarse and shrill with him last time and the Matthew Hay who was now received in the homes of lairds and other titled folk wanted a partner like the gracious lady-wives he met there. Still less did he want clash about the banknotes, for he had this marriage of Mary's to Sir William Cuningham to consider and the chance for himself to be kin to that simple aristocrat and in a position perhaps to 'invest' some of the Caprintoun money for him.

If all his recent and ongoing misdemeanours were to come to light at this stage, the heritor ranks would close against him. Mary, for all her gentle ways, would not be acceptable as the lady of Caprintoun if a funny-begotten nephew or niece was known to be toddling around the yard of the bare steading at Ploughlands with a rabble of illiterate cousins, child of a rough young kitchen maid. Nor would the Cuninghams and the Eglintons, who were kin, welcome a convicted forger to their family. And when the gossips were about it they would like enough make the most of his guiding hand in the smuggling and the way they said it was changing from sport to violence.

He sat up very late in the parlour that night where, on the evening before, he had seen himself, in the not-too-distant future, entertaining all the fine folk of the shire. He sat now staring into a glass of

64

French brandy. He grew more agitated by the hour at the thought of the insignificant Lizzie Wilson spoiling all that for him. It was not to be borne.

When the glass was empty he laid it on the mantel-shelf and went outside. He skirted past the sleeping bothy to the barn. Inside, two rats scuttled across his feet as he groped about on a shelf for a small packet.

Hay wrestled with his problem for a week as he went about his affairs betraying nothing of the tumult churning inside him. On the Tuesday evening he flattered and teased Miss Dunlop, a house-guest at Holms, and her friend Miss Walker, the minister's daughter. They giggled as he played a hand of cards with them and shook their heads over his flirty ways when he left them and retired to bed.

The next day, March 16th of 1780, Matthew Hay tucked into his pocket the poke of arsenic he had taken from his barn, where it was kept to kill rats. He walked by the winding river-path alongside the Irvine and up the slope to Ploughlands farm. The wind was snell but the shivering of him inside his checked wool plaid was not from its cut. He reached the yard. Two families of Wilsons lived there and although it was Lizzie's immediate family he had business with today, he called first on her brother's house, chatted briefly, as he would on any other casual visit, then mentioned that he had a thirst on him for a drink of good fresh water but that he would get it when he called next door. Then, having shown nothing untoward or hurried in his manner, he left that cottage and went to the other where he found the door ajar on Lizzie's kitchen. He knocked and went inside.

Apart from Lizzie's old doited mother, prematurely aged with a wasting illness and sitting now nodding, half asleep, but puffing a pipe of tobacco at the hearth, only the girl was in the room. He saw with part-relief part-terror that a pot of cream porridge was on the fire, and felt that surely fate had cleared his path. But he tempted her once again with the offer of Edinburgh, and she refused him.

'I've a fierce thirst on me the day Lizzie, go you and bring me a drink of fresh-drawn water. What's in the house'll have stood too long. Get it cool from the well, lass.'

She didn't like being ordered, but he was, after all, the bien master of Holms, so she flounced a little sullenly from the kitchen to fetch him his jar of water.

65

A kind of cold inevitability was on Matthew now. There was no drawing back. He made certain the old woman was too far gone in her doze to see what he was up to, then he emptied his arsenic into the porridge and stirred it with the spirtle. Lizzie came back with the well-water, set it down to him and began to put her word in for some money to be going on with, to buy a delicacy or two for her fragile condition. But he was in a hurry now and, taking time only to promise her some the next day, stooped out of the house and walked swiftly down the path, dreading, yet hoping, that he had seen the last of Lizzie Wilson.

But Lizzie did not die of the bitter porridge. The whole family ailed it was true, and all of them gravely, mother, father and sister, likewise a pair of luckless visitors from the village who called and were invited to a sup of the broth. But it was her father, the gudeman of Ploughlands and Hay's grieve, and her mother, the old body smoking at the ingle, who were taken worst, and in a few days both were dead.

Matthew Hay hovered about the steading, hoping desperately that the family would be judged to have been smit by a food poisoning, earnestly offering help with the questioning and any medicaments that might help the rest of the farm-folk still sick. He seemed as shocked about the whole matter as the lave of Dundonald folk. And in a few days he was more shocked than any of them for it was clear to him by then, that murder was being suggested and that he was the prime suspect.

Matthew Hay was arrested and carried off to the Ayr Tolbooth to wait until the evidence was gathered and sifted, and a case prepared against him for his trial in September.

He was tried for murder at the Ayr Assizes on 6th September 1780, before his old acquaintances, Lord Braxfield and his chess-opponent Lord Kames. Neighbours, servants and the family at Ploughlands witnessed for and against him. Although none were eye-witnesses, the evidence was damning and he was found 'Guilty, by a great plurality of voices.' He was sentenced to be hanged by the neck on the Muir of Ayr on 13th October 1780.

Hay claimed from first to last that he was innocent. He went to the gallows dressed in sober black, as if for the Sabbath service, but some deep sense of finality and occasion may have dredged up memories of the kirk-disciplines of his youth for he was heard to sing in a low voice a portion of the sinner's Psalm. 'Create in me a clean heart and renew a right spirit within me ... deliver me from blood-guiltiness, O God,' as he mounted the scaffold steps.

As he dangled there, through that long October afternoon, some recalled the scene in the courtroom when sentence had been pronounced. Henry Home, Lord Kames, had sat in stern and gloomy formality and added his postscript in flat doom-laden tones ...

'Only you and God know your innocence or guilt, Matthew Hay, but your trial has been fair and the evidence given against you has convinced the jury,' he declared ... and then leaned forward grimly over the bench.

'Checkmate, Matthew, eh?' he said.

Of the survivors of that afternoon at Ploughlands farmhouse, Lizzie Wilson's sister was a lifelong invalid from her poisoning and the Dundonald visitors suffered recurring bouts of illness. Lizzie herself bore a healthy full-term son and defiantly gave him the name James Hay. He grew up to become a hawker in and around Kilmarnock where he lived in poverty and fathered several ill-doing sons and daughters, who neither rose to their grandsire's erstwhile prosperity nor fell into quite the depth of his wickedness.

Hay went to the gallows declaring his innocence and there have been those who believed that there was some kind of conspiracy by those who first encouraged his social ambitions and then, when these became overweaning, used the murder charge to be rid of him. But 'Checkmate' is the tale generally accepted as being closest to the truth.

Although the misdeeds of Matthew Hay have been fully and officially documented, his story has always been accompanied by apocryphal anecdote and rumour. There is much more to the tale than is told here, some of it true, some of it probably fictional. There was the fate of Mary Hay, said to have died of her disappointed marriage hopes, the details of the forging in France, the violent death of Hay's father, his own connection with the previous murder of an exciseman, even his standing with the lairds and other authorities, which allowed him to escape punishment over earlier transgressions. The Earl of Eglinton himself once interposed on Hay's behalf, pointing out his value to the community as a model farmer. But perhaps the strangest post-script to his death came years afterwards. His family had requested, and been granted at the time of his death, his coffined body for burial. The interment duly took place and some years later the grave was, for some reason, opened and the coffin found to contain only a man's weight in gravelly sand. Kelso Hunter the Dundonald artist/shoemaker told of taking home a handful of that sand as proof of the hoax. Whether it was officially or locally conceived no one knows.

The Meal that Cost Him Dear

One year when the harvest had been poor the farmers of Kyle had to raise their prices above what they had been for several years previous. As ever, poor folk grumbled and paid up.

There was one youthful farmer with a greed for siller, who thought himself as shrewd and canny a merchant as he was a farmer and, being the only source of meal in two parishes, put his price up higher than anyone else in outlying areas.

One day a poor widow-woman, with a quiver of hungry bairns at home, came to him for her winter bag of meal and found herself short of his asking price by a shilling. She begged for a week or two to pay, but the astute young farmer was of the opinion that kindness to the poor was a sort of foolishness. He insisted on the motto 'no price, no meal.'

'I'm but the shillin' short,' she pleaded. 'Can you no' trust me?'

'I dinnae trust nobody,' he said pompously, almost righteously, and loudly enough for a passing soldier to hear as he made his way towards his barracks in Kilmarnock.

The soldier was a good fellow and he stopped and asked what the argument was. They told him.

'How much are you short, Mistress?' he asked.

'Just the yin shillin'', she said sadly.

The soldier felt in his pouch and pulled out a coin.

'See here, Farmer Stint. Here's a perfectly good shilling. Tak' it and gie the wife her meal.' And he tossed him the coin scornfully. The grateful woman becked and bobbed him a curtsy and hurried off with her bag. The soldier went on his way to Kilmarnock, the farmer chuckled as he added the woman's money and the soldier's coin to the pile in the tankard on his mantel shelf.

Next day the soldier arrived back from Kilmarnock with two sergeant-companions, seized the protesting farmer and marched him back to the headquarters in Kilmarnock where he found to his dismay that he had taken the King's Shilling and would gather his next harvest only when he had served out his time with the soldiery.

The Falcon, the Spider and
the Empty Crown

Young Lord Robert of Annandale had emerged from the forest one day in the year 1271 and was riding home through Carrick from his adventurous years of soldiering in the Holy Crusades. He had been weary when he set out that morning after a night in a hillside cave, but now that he could feel the soft green grass under his horse's hooves and see the drifting Scottish mists about him, his spirits revived. He sat tall in his saddle, threw back his handsome head and began to sing across the moorland, believing that he was alone for miles around.

But he was not, for the young widow Marjory Kilconceth was out with her falcons and her attending squires and ladies. It was over two years since she had lost her husband Adam, in the self-same wars as Robert of Annandale had survived, she was young, her heart well healed and it was a merry party which sped over the brow of a hill and spied the single horseman. The lady held up a hand to halt her attendants and put a finger to her lips as she paused to listen to the lusty singing voice and to watch the stranger with the proud seat and gallant bearing, ride across their path quite unaware that he was being observed.

In an impulsive moment then the young Countess of Carrick bade her knights and servants fan out and ride round to encircle the rider, while she and her ladies spurred their horses forward quickly to make a smaller ring round him, laughing as they closed in.

'You are our prisoner, good Knight!' she cried. 'Pray tell us your name before we allow you to pass on.'

He doffed his hat with the woodcock's feather in it, and she saw the fair hair that curled tightly round his brow. And she saw his melting smile.

'I am Robert Bruce of Annandale, my lady. And am I to know the name of my captor?'

'Marjory, widow to Adam of Kilconceth.'

He knew now who she was and that she lived not many miles away at the Castle of Turnberry. And she knew now who he was, and that he was greatly honoured in these parts for his prowess in the fighting for the Holy Sepulchre.

'You must come to Turnberry and have food and shelter for a day or two before you take your journey home again,' she invited him.

Robert was as susceptible to charm as the next man and Lady Marjory had it in good measure. A few days' rest in such company would have been balm indeed to his tired warrior soul. But a warning bell rang in his wary head when he remembered that this Carrick beauty was a ward of the King, Alexander III, who would certainly resent the faintest whiff of suggestion that she was being courted outwith some consenting arrangement with him. And so Robert declined the pressing invitation now.

Marjory tossed her head, not much liking to be thwarted, and at a signal her party closed round the knight with mock threat and fairly forced him, half-laughing half-protesting, to ride with her to Turnberry.

There romance overcame caution and after a few days Robert Bruce, 7th Lord of Annandale, was wed to Marjory, Countess of Carrick, by a nervous priest who foresaw the fury of the king and trembled for his part in the marriage.

Alexander was angry, for he took seriously his duty as protector of the widow of one of his warriors, a wealthy land-owning young woman prey to the advances of any adventurer. He swiftly seized Turnberry Castle and estates to keep them from marauding hands. But when he understood that Marjory had not been importuned into marriage against her will, he was pacified by a substantial sum of peace money.

Robert therefore passed into possession, through Marjory, of the Earldom of Carrick and of Turnberry Castle with all its fair lands. There is no written record that the first of their twelve children was born at Turnberry, but the boy who in time became King Robert the Bruce of Scotland had so many associations with the place and returned there so constantly after both triumphs and disasters that old tellers of his tale down the ages, judge that he saw Turnberry always as 'home' and had probably been born there.

As children, Robert and his brothers and sisters played contentedly on the green fields to the landward side of the Castle and on the white-gold sands of the Atlantic shore below it, and they grew up looking out at Ailsa Craig, Arran and the Mull of Kintyre.

It would have seemed good to many men who inherited such a keep and the peaceful rolling countryside of its estates bordering the Atlantic sea, to enjoy the working and hunting of his extensive lands; and perhaps to send out small merchant ships to bring back rich goods and trade with France and Ireland.

In his early manhood this second Robert, who in his turn became Earl of Carrick, lived peacefully enough at Turnberry. Like other Scottish lords he had sworn his fealty to Edward I of England. Their own King Alexander III was now dead, having been thrown from his horse and plunged over a cliff at Kinghorn, and leading Scottish nobles were now squabbling for his crown in feeble disarray. And so Edward of England had become overlord of Scotland also.

Then not far from Turnberry itself rose the great William Wallace, called the Warden of Scotland. He excited the patriotic fervour of warm-blooded Scots all over the south and for a time the young Robert threw his strength behind him when it seemed that Wallace might oust Edward and his 'Southrons' and make Scotland an independent kingdom again.

But Robert's allegiance in those early days was a fickle thing. It swung back and forth several times between the Scottish freedom fighters and the Hammer of the Scots and there were those who accused him of making sure his family's future was as powerful as its past, by planting a foot firmly in each camp.

Perhaps Robert matured during the time when Wallace was painstakingly welding the Scots together as a nation, and while the power-struggles among the nobles continued after his death; perhaps he was simply inspired by William Wallace; or perhaps he began to see himself emerging incredibly as one of the two main contenders for the Scottish crown itself. The other claimant who was grandson to a former king, John Baliol, was John Comyn, known in Scotland as 'Red' Comyn.

Legend surrounding the rivalry suggests that Bruce did indeed have his sights set on the throne and that when the two men encountered each other in the Convent of the Minorite Friars at Dumfries they quarrelled over their contending claims. The chapel was empty except for the two nobles. Companions outside heard raised voices and the clash of steel, then were startled to see Robert of Carrick rush out from the church in wild agitation.

'I must flee for I doubt I've slain Red Comyn!'

'Doubt!' scoffed Kirkpatrick of Closeburn, one of those attending Bruce. 'There's no room for doubt. Bide here and I'll mak' siccar.'

Kirkpatrick was as sure as his word. Whatever hurt Bruce actually did Comyn, he was dead for certain when Kirkpatrick left him.

71

There was no other aspirant to the throne now, and two months later Bruce had himself crowned at Scone with a simple circlet of gold, but not seated for the ceremony on the ancient Coronation Stone of Destiny (said to have once been Jacob's 'pillow' during his 'ladder' dream) for it had already been seized by Edward and placed beneath the English Coronation Chair as a symbol of Scottish vassalage.

But Edward I of England was still true master and overlord of Scotland and the newly crowned King Robert the Bruce was skulking in his own countryside with English soldiers searching glens and mountainsides to flush him out and take his life. Tales say that six times he emerged to strike a blow for independence and was six times driven back into hiding. The blessing of the Pope was on Edward, for Robert had been excommunicated for the murder of Comyn in a consecrated house of God.

Makars tell us all we know of the next chapter of Bruce's progress towards real kingship. Their songs say that while he was being sought in Scotland among hills and valleys Robert was actually on the island of Rathlin off the Irish coast, restlessly waiting to hear that the first step in capturing Scotland for the Scots, had been taken by his lieutenants. He was a man of action and weary of waiting, dejected that word did not come. He was tempted to believe his cause was lost before it had ever really begun. And the best-known of all the tales of Scotland's King Robert the Bruce is that, while he grew impatient lying in the sheltering cottage on Rathlin almost ready to give up his crown, leave his homeland and go to fight the Saracens, he noticed one morning a spider trying to spin its thread from one roof beam to another. Six times it made the attempt and six times it failed.

'Six times I have been driven back from my purpose by the Southrons and six times this spider has failed to fasten his web. If he tries and succeeds at his seventh time, then I too will try again.'

The spider tried again and won, and Bruce took renewed heart. And then the tidings came of the first success for his campaign.

That was the taking of Brodick Castle on the island of Arran, and when he had word of the victory Robert joined his small troop and tiny fleet of galleys at Arran. There he walked on the shore and brooded over how to gather together his own Turnberry men living across the water, how to rally them behind him. How great, he wondered, was the loyalty of the men of his estate who had not seen their Earl-King for several long years now? Was the Castle perhaps

72

garrisoned by occupying English troops? At last he sent over a small boat by night with a messenger disguised as a minstrel. The man whose name was Cuthbert was to spy out the Turnberry land and light a beacon if the way was clear for an invasion of the Scottish mainland by her own King.

All that evening Bruce watched from Arran for the signal from Turnberry and at last he saw a fire burning brightly above the opposite shore, and put to sea. But when he landed Cuthbert assured him that there had been no signalling beacon and that the local people were too afraid of the powerful English garrison to rise for Robert Bruce with his small army. There was a skirmish outside the walls of Turnberry with victory for neither side and Bruce withdrew honourably to gather more support for his next attempt to gain a foothold.

He wandered the hills of Carrick, winning a promise from a laird here and a feudal landlord there, to join him when the call came. And many stories surround the roaming in Ayrshire in those years of the king-without-a-kingdom.

Bruce was ever constant in his prayers and he knelt one day seeking guidance in a quiet clearing in an Ayrshire woodland. He raised his head from meditation to see three men approaching him so stealthily that he knew they hunted him for his life. He took the bow and arrow from his page, aimed steadily and killed one man, then with his own short sword dispatched the other two. Word of the deed was carried by the hero-worshipping page and soon Bruce's name was on the tongue of every Ayrshireman who knew any more of life than what went on in his own kailpatch. And after his next exploit it echoed even further across the lowlands, taken by pedlars and wayfarers on their wanderings. A troop of Southrons with bloodhounds had been sent to hunt him and he had been warned of the chase by a peasant woman drawing water from a burn. The men were making for a small bridge over the stream and Bruce waited their arrival there hidden in a thick grove of alders. They came singly and the King drew each of the unsuspecting men among the trees and killed or stunned them one by one.

There was no more peaceful wandering for Robert after that. The next pursuit followed swiftly and was led by an English Commander who came hunting him with more sleuth-hounds. The party could not be shaken off and Bruce was almost exhausted when he found another burn and confused the scent to the dogs by plunging his way along its bed, until they were curling themselves helplessly in panting circles in and out of the water, far behind him.

The end nearly came yet again, this time as the result of conspiracy, when three English soldiers disguised as countrymen made friendly overtures when they encountered the King with his brother Edward and travelled with the two to a small inn. There they fell on the Bruces, killing Edward, but Robert, enraged at their duplicity and the death of his faithful brother, took on all three and killed them.

He fled into hiding again. But Scotland had begun to look to this determined monarch for it seemed just possible that he might lead them to true sovereignty and be perhaps as great a king as their lost Alexander. Pockets of support grew until Bruce had a sizeable army at his back.

In the sometimes chivalrous spirit of the day, a set-piece battle was arranged to take place at Loudon Hill in Cuninghame. The Scottish army was smaller but Bruce's tactics in the deployment of his soldiers and the use of their skills with pike and spear won the day. The English were driven off and retreated to Ayr Castle to which the Scots followed and laid siege for some weeks of that summer of 1307. But troops came to the relief of the Southrons and the autumn saw Bruce withdrawn, for the time being, to the hills.

News came then of the death of Edward I, The Hammer of the Scots. The new Edward was but a weak echo of his father and Bruce knew that his hour had struck. The story of men trooping to his banner from all over the country, of his mopping up of garrison after garrison of the occupying troops, of the final famous victory at Bannockburn and of Robert the Bruce coming into the full kingship of his people ... that story does not belong to Ayrshire lore, but to the history of all Scotland.

Later tales told by poets and minstrels however, take King Robert back into Ayrshire. He bestowed money and lands on the Benedectines of Crossraguel Abbey; and to a holy community in Prestwyk he granted the acres known as Freelands. He founded hospices and visited humble peasant folk who had sheltered him long ago. And in his latter years when he suffered the dread disease of leprosy, tradition records that he was treated with the waters of a healing well at Kingcase in Prestwyk. They say he gained great comfort and benefit from them and so endowed a lazarus-house there for the shelter and care of eight lepers, each one to have eight bolls of meal and eight merks a year to provision him in his misfortune.

74

Bannockburn in 1314 had confirmed Robert Bruce resoundingly as King of Scotland, in thrall to no other. His renown in war had earned him his crown. His wisdom in peace brought him reputation as a merciful and progressive ruler. He rebuilt castles, towns and small country communities destroyed or damaged in war and he brought together men of sense and purpose to form a simple parliament for law-making and dispensing justice.

The great equestrian statue of Bruce stands at Bannockburn near Stirling; his heart lies at Melrose; his body at Dunfermline Abbey under the square tower topped with his name in stone round its four sides, and alongside William Wallace he stands guard at the entrance to Edinburgh Castle. Stirling, Melrose, Dunfermline, Edinburgh boast links with him, King Robert the Bruce, of all Scotland.

But his roots were in Ayrshire.

He was born and reared there and he grew there to maturity. It was the men of Ayrshire who rallied to his cause in its green days, and the women who fed and sheltered him as an outlaw. It was there he went to find relief and comfort in the days of his weakness when he was near to death. Life had come full circle, since that day fifty-eight years before, when a spirited girl riding in Carrick with a falcon on her wrist had laughingly captured young Robert of Annandale and carried him off to her castle to bear him a son.

A modern analyst could spend an interesting hour studying the man who, in his early days, vacillated five or six times between vowing fealty to Edward I of England and conversely fighting and plotting against him. It is puzzling too that in 1303 he became Sheriff of Lanark and Constable of Ayr Castle for Edward and attended his parliament at St. Andrews; and that while he was still under homage to the English King he was working against him, in league with the Archbishop of St. Andrews. Perhaps he was trying, at that stage, to ensure that he had a reputation for loyalty to whoever would eventually win the power struggle. But there is no doubt that, as soon as he saw his own chance of emerging as king or perhaps of simply making Scotland independent again, he wavered no more.

Other sources, supported by Tom Weir in *Scottish Islands*, locate the 'spider' story at the King's Cave, Blackwaterfoot Arran. H. W. Meikle, other writers and the people of Rathlin claim the source I have used. The story is as likely to be true of an Irish as a Scottish spider.

Josey, the Lazy Worker to Mister Fairlie

In days long gone by, there was a worthy (or maybe he was an unworthy) of the district between Symington and Kilmarnock. He was a poet of sorts and he always had a long drouth in him that took a deal of satisfying. He was, for a time, in the service of Mr. Fairlie of Fairlie House, not far from the clachan of Romford, where he was a ditcher on the estate. He worked quite hard at keeping his ditches clean and straight and was paid 'so much' a day.

Most of the time Josey was a fair worker and earned his bread, but there were other times when he was overcome by such thirst that he had to throw down his spade into a hedge-row and go to the ale-house to satisfy it. These orgies would be followed by a spiritual withdrawal to his garret to act the makar at his versifying.

One such drouth came on him just at harvest time when it was of prime importance to keep the fields from being water-logged. When Mr. Fairlie discovered his absence he was infuriated and instructed his grieve that when Josey did put in an appearance he was to be chased for his life off the estate.

Ten days later Josey picked up his spade and came whistling and singing back to his ditch-digging as jaunty as if he had never been absent. The grieve was a gentle giant of a man and told him sadly that Mr. Fairlie wanted no more of him and would he please leave the place and not come back.

'Who said so?' demanded an aggrieved and angry Josey.

'The Master his-self left word.'

'Aweel, no harm to you, Jamuck, I'll see the laird myself.' The butler was less gentle but firmer and would have shut the door on Josey's face had his foot not been wedged in the door jamb.

'I'm come to see Master Fairlie and if I stay here till midnight, see him I will.' And Josey folded his arms purposefully. Mr. Fairlie heard him and came out.

'Go about your business, man, there's no work for you at Fairlie.'

'What am I to do then?'

'Whatsoever you please, but not here. Away you go and sing your fancy ballads.' Josey stood still with his shaggy head cocked to one side.

'Aye, I'll dae that,' he said after a pause, 'and I'll come back and gi'e you the first hearing, Master.' And he chuckled wickedly, withdrew

his foot and went slowly back to his garret to chew the end of his pen.

By evening he was back at Fairlie. He had no need of knocker or bell this time, for he stood on the wide step and sang lustily so that every word floated up to the open window of the dining apartment above.

On the green banks of Irvine bides Fairlie of Fairlie
Who speaks godly things and yet does them but rarely
The poor of his workers they walk footed-barely
Being robbed of their dues
By yon Fairlie of Fairlie.

When in the low regions, my! how he will fret!
There'll no' be rich pickings from farms he'll can get
The Devil will scold him and roast him right sairly
And Hell will resound with the shrieks of old Fairlie.

There were several other more scandalsome verses with just enough truth in them to make Fairlie the butt of local sniggers and leave him determined not to have them bruited round the parish. He came to the door in a passion and roared at Josey to get back at first light to his ditching and to hand over the paper of tale-telling verses.

But while Josey was glad enough in these hard times to get his job back, he wasn't so soft as to give up every copy of his song. And Fairlie found the words so ill that Josey kept them as something of an insurance from time to time afterwards for wee bits of holiday from his labours with the spade.

The Shot in the Eglinton Woods

It was one of the ironies of the rude 18th Century in Scotland that more than one guardian of the law in a particular area of its enforcement was himself a law breaker in another. Take the likes of Mungo Campbell, an excise officer by profession who, they say, was merciless in his pursuit of the smugglers around Troon. He was as harsh with the small boys who waved their coloured jerseys from dune top to dune top, like washing on a line, to signal the arrival of an illicit cargo of tea or brandy from the Isle of Man, as he was with their fathers and brothers who received and stored it away. But Mungo had his own besetting sin in his unlawful practice of putting a free hare or rabbit or a brace of birds into his mother's yawning cooking-pot ... yawning because Mungo was one of a family of twenty-four souls, well connected with gentry folk, but poor as many a cotman with a kailpatch. He favoured most often for his crime, part of the home estate of Alexander Montgomerie, the 10th Earl of Eglinton, and there he roamed with his gun and his catch-sack whenever he was free of his excise duties. His step on the leaf-mould under the trees was silent from years of practice, and his finger on the trigger fast and sure, to pick off any plump partridge or pigeon which gave itself away by rustling the trees, or any rabbit bold enough to scuttle across his path.

Alexander of Eglinton was a liberal-minded man in his time, one of the new breed of Improving Countrymen concerned for the well-being and progress of the farmers who paid him rent and the labourers who tilled their rigs. Indeed he was so concerned to see progressive ways applied on his estates that when, on one occasion, he was called out to a duel in which he could well die, he wrote what he thought might be a farewell letter to his brother and heir, Archibald Montgomerie, bidding him 'mind how he drilled his turnips'.

As well as having this eccentric, though sensible, order of priorities and being fair and popular, he was just as mindful of his own rights and privileges as of those of the men who worked his land. One of these privileges was to preserve the shooting in his own Eglinton Woods, near Ardrossan, for himself and any guests he might invite to be of his party.

78

It was therefore with great displeasure that he heard from time to time that Mungo Campbell, the Saltcoats exciseman, was helping himself to Eglinton woodpigeon and hare. He was not so incensed that he hunted Campbell down to confront him with his misdemeanours, but he was pleased to come face to face with the man at his stolen pleasure one afternoon, gun in hand and partridge in bag. The Earl's tongue did not spare the poacher but, being a reasonable man, he told himself that though this was not a first offence it was certainly a first catching and did not warrant punishing. Besides the man's promise, freely given, might be more binding than the threat of dire consequence which might simply prove a challenge to a red-blooded man.

'You've no right to sport for game in the woods here, Mungo Campbell. Many a laird would have you face the courts or at least have you dismissed your post with the Excise.' Campbell shifted uneasily.

Servants at Eglinton had it later that it was then that Lord Alexander minded the twenty-six mouths to be fed under the threadbare thatch of the Campbell cottage and thought to be easy on the poacher.

'If you give me your word on keeping the trespass law and troubling these woods no more we'll say nothing further on the matter. There's other places for your shooting. But give me a solemn promise Campbell. Have I your oath, sir?'

'An' you take no notice of this day, milord, you have my word on it I'll no prowl these parts again.'

'Mind you don't for you've a steady position to think of, and an example to set, keeping others from law breaking.'

Whether Campbell seriously meant to keep his promise or was only smooth-tongueing an angry laird, whether it was from need or only challenge, the temptation to go a-poaching overcame him again after a few weeks abstinence. Soon he was making as free as ever with Eglinton game. All that year he took from the Earl's coverts at his pleasure, without discovery. And then the month of October came round.

Although he knew quite well that the Earl had guests from the south with him for the shooting, Mungo ventured yet again into the parklands at Ardrossan. But this time, as he padded softly along one path, he was confronted suddenly by the Earl coming out of a cross-track near the boundary of the estate land, having left his carriage on the road nearby with a footman, and being met by a stable-boy bringing a horse to him for the exercise of riding home. Lord Alexander was angry. Campbell dodged on to the adjacent sands just outwith the private woodland but Eglinton followed and faced him there.

'Your promise is little worth then it seems, Mungo Campbell.'

'My promise, my lord? What promise was that?' bluffed Mungo.

'Fine you know that, sir.'

Highland grandsires had left a dour mark on Mungo Campbell.

'I cannae mind a promise milord,' he said roughly.

'I did not proceed against you for the sake of your oath then, Mungo Campbell but I shall do so this time. Be pleased to hand me your gun.'

'You cannot have my gun.'

'Then I must take it from you.' It was a brave threat from the bespectacled scholar of Eglinton.

'That you'll no' do, sir, as long's I live. You may have the law on

A SHOT IN EGLINTON WOODS

80

me as you will, but this gun is my belonging and I mean to keep it.'

The Earl moved on Campbell.

'Stand back, my lord, an you value your life for I will fire do you touch this gun.'

Eglinton came on, watched by gaping servants who had by now heard raised voices and come to see what was amiss. More than one of these local men had tales to tell of the exciseman's temper and they feared for their lord. He made a last appeal.

'Don't be foolish, Campbell. You'll not fire.'

'I will fire.'

The Earl then called for his own fowling-piece from the carriage and, while he waited, he advanced again across the sandy ground. The poacher held his gun steady but took a step back and tripped on a boulder yirdfast in the ground behind him. Even among those who watched, there were some who said that the stumble set off the trigger and others who swore it was pulled deliberately. Whatever the truth of accident or intent, the consequence was that Earl Alexander took the entire loading of shot from the exciseman's piece and fell bleeding heavily from mortal wounds.

He struggled to his feet, the coolest man in the confused assembly, and walked falteringly towards his carriage. But his strength failed him, he was helped to the machine and was taken swiftly home to Eglinton Castle. With a last effort he told those around him that he had intended only to frighten the poacher into sense, and that his fowling piece had not been loaded. He died later that day and the gun was indeed found to be empty.

Mungo Campbell was brought to trial for murder, found guilty and sentenced to be hanged at the Edinburgh Grassmarket in April 1770. He forestalled the hangman by doing the job himself in his cell. His body was to have been sent for anatomising as was the custom after a hanging, but at his friends' request it was delivered to them for burial. A rabble later dug it up and sported with it as if it were a raggy-doll until they were tired. To save it further shame his friends took the tattered remnant in a small boat and carried it far out from shore where they quietly let the last of Mungo Campbell sink into the sea.

There is an eerie, legendary postscript to this well-documented tale. Alexander, 10th Earl of Eglinton, was, at the time of his death, betrothed to a daughter of the Maxwell family of Pollok House near Eastwood parish. During the months prior to the wedding he was a regular visitor at Pollok and occupied, on these occasions, an upstairs bedchamber of the house. One day in October 1769 a servant there saw him enter the mansion and step lightly up the staircase towards his room. The servant went down to the kitchens to have a meal prepared for the unexpected and unannounced arrival, but when it was ready the house was searched for Alexander, in vain. It is claimed that later enquiries set the time of the servant's sighting as being exactly the hour of Alexander's fatal shooting at Ardrossan, nearly thirty miles away.

While Earl Alexander was one of the 'Improvers' in the estate management of his time, and laboured with great seriousness and energy to raise the standard of his tenants' living, it is his dramatic and tragic death which is best remembered of him.

The Bewitching of Margaret Stewart

The peasant folk of Ochiltree stood in rigs, at cot doors and around the village well, herds laid halting hands on the heads of animals they were bringing in from the outfield and shawled women held excited bairns close to their skirts. They had fallen still from their labours, or silent from their gossip, overawed at the sight of the cavalcade that was sweeping up towards Ochiltree House.

The man at the centre of the procession of foot and horse-men rode on a richly caparisoned gelding with gleaming leathers wrought intricately with silver, and marvellous ribbon braidings in tail and mane. The cuffs, lacings and facings of his own apparel were made of rich stuffs, with bands of scarlet and blue taffeta fastened with gold studs. His white hands glittered with rings, and a jewel of precious stones set in marvellously fashioned gold was on his breast. Soft fur trimmed his collar and cap and sat warm and kind against his neck.

Different folk on his route that day saw different facets of his peacocky style and whispered together in amazement that such a fancy-got-up man should be visiting the sober, godly and much respected family at Ochiltree.

But the man John himself, had no thought for the verdict of the plainfolk of an Ayrshire moorland. For he was a lover, paying court. He cared, that day, for only the verdict of the lady of his heart at Ochiltree Castle. Every item in his vestments and the beribboning and polish of his retinue, had been chosen to dazzle and captivate the high-spirited and delightful Margaret Stewart, daughter of Andrew Stewart, Lord Ochiltree. There was the added secret hope in his youthful lusty heart that a union with that lovely lady might some day see his own descendents enter the line of succession to the Scottish throne, for Ochiltree was one of the highest ranking nobles in the land and an implacable opponent of its present occupant, whom John also dearly wished to see ousted. That was a lesser ambition, for the present, than winning the lady, but John was experienced enough to know that it would make valuable compensation to fall back on when the first flush of married passion had subsided.

The procession arrived at Ochiltree. Andrew Stewart was out riding across his lands, the ladies of the house were resting or out walking in the garden. John's retinue was quartered and he himself stood now in his chamber window overlooking the garden and the moors beyond.

Then he saw the lady of his love plucking flowers and walking among the blossoming trees. She was very young and quite lovely, her thick hair hanging in a shining mane, her skin the colour of cream and roses. And the watcher knew that his first glimpse of her some weeks before and his memories since, had not played him false.

Her suitor looked in the glass and adjusted his plum-coloured velvet doublet. Then he changed his mind about its colour and found another more richly broidered and hastily unlaced the first.

He drew in a deep breath and called on all the Powers of Light and Darkness, Good and Evil, God and the Devil, whichever Master he needed for this endeavour which was to bring him so much. And in a bewitching aura of gallantry, handsomeness, boldness, manliness and youth, he went down the staircase to introduce himself to the beautiful creature in the garden whom he had seen only at a distance on that previous visit.

A young girl sat on a boulder by a gently lifting willow tree beside the river. She wore a plain grey dress demurely kirtled in periwinkle blue, just the colour of her own bright eyes. She watched a drift of crowfoot flowers in the running shallows all standing like little soldiers facing a patch of sunlight on the river.

Suddenly a pebble plopped into the water at her feet jawping her dress with water and she turned to find young Simon Brodie in plain breeches and open sark standing smiling above her on the bank. He was a slim youth, brown-haired, brown-eyed, brown-skinned and he had loved Margaret Stewart with an understanding and uncomplicated heart since they were children. She laughed and he leapt down beside her, landing on both feet and compounded the water-splash with mud. He kissed her firmly and pulled her to her feet.

'Come wi' me, Margaret, and I'll show you a badger-sett I came on the day and a wee clump of four-leaf clovers.' They were walking arms entwined now, along the path, 'four-leafy clovers are luck, you ken, luck in love.'

'Believing in luck's sinful superstition, Simon Brodie. If you marry me some day, you'll need to not believe in suchlike matters. Good's good and bad's bad and there's no such thing as casting spells or witching, no' for Christian folk anyways ... You'll maybe not wed me, mind,' she tossed a teasing head, 'but you'd best be good, no matter.'

'Och I'll wed you, right enough,' said Simon, kissing her lightly again. 'I'll have to go to the College first mind, and come out a dominie or maybe a minister, but I'll wed you after that.' And she knew he would. His father might be but the Cumnock schoolmaster and live in modest simplicity and her father might be the great Lord Ochiltree but Andrew Stewart was a godly man who prized virtue, booklearning, and character before wealth, and if his daughter chose a poor scholar for her husband then, although he would not insult the lad with undue patronage, he would find ways to prevent them living in poverty.

The two young people saw the badger-sett and watched a dipper bird flying low along the river pausing now and then to bob on a boulder. They saw the patch of clover and then, heart-sure and contented, they swung clasped hands as they walked across the little river bridge and up the slope to Ochiltree. They took a last kiss, confident of tomorrow, and parted.

'Mind now, Simon, and dinnae tamper no more with clover spells. You'll no' win Margaret Stewart that way,' she called after him laughingly and ran into the Ochiltree garden where the gaudy John saw her from his window. Then she picked a bunch of flowers for her bedchamber.

They say the Devil favoured the visitor to Ochiltree and spun a glittering halo round him as he came down the stairs to meet Margaret Stewart that day, and that he cast a glammer over the girl. They say too that Satan took away the memory of Simon Brodie from her heart as if he had never been, that he made the other gay and companionable throughout his visit, mature and infinitely desirable and that Margaret Stewart of the innocent heart and lovely countenance was utterly bewitched.

She waved aside her mystified father's gentle protestations and met his mindings of Simon with blank incomprehension in her face. But this was, after all, a notable match and, if it also gladdened his lassie's heart, then as a fond father he could do no less than give it his blessing and settle on them the lush rigs of Pennymore farm as the first part of her dowry.

And away to Edinburgh from Ochiltree, at the end of that week, rode the lusty bridegroom to prepare for his wedding — a very different man from the one who had first set foot at Andrew Stewart's home on the original visit a month or two previously. He thought now on that other man ...

He had come then a weary jaded man. He had been tired after a lifetime of work as a priest, of study in the Latin, in theology, in the disturbing works of Jerome and Augustine. He had toiled in the French galleys for his seditious views, laboured over plans for schooling of the common people. He had preached in Geneva, exhausted himself in abortive debate with Ninian Wyngate and with Quentin Kennedy the Papist Abbot of Crossraguel, and in the historic Interviews with the thrawn Lady at Holyrood (confrontations not yet finished but in which he was already inwardly and angrily conscious that she often bettered him in tact and even logic).

That day he had come riding wearily along the track to Ochiltree, clad in worn and sober black, attended by only one man. He had been an ageing and souring widower soon to turn sixty and with little to look forward to but his stern allegiance to the bleak kirk he had created, to pulpit thunderings, to long evenings under guttering candles with his books, and then to his narrow lonely bed. Ochiltree had urged him to a week of rest in the country and he had come to try to gain a little energy to revitalise his work.

As he passed up towards the castle he had caught sight of a young girl, mounted on a cream palfrey and attended by four ladies, coming towards him. Both parties had moved slowly and he had ample time to study the fair face and imprint it on his mind before they had passed each other by. He had bowed but her attention had been on a lad waving to her from the moorland at the roadside and she had scarcely been aware of him. But he had known who she was and that during his visit she was to be from home staying with her mother's kin.

During that week he had heard much from her father and from serving men and women, of the mild and happy spirit of Margaret Stewart and of her unrebellious acceptance of the new religion.

'She's a Christian lassie and it doesnae matter whether she worships under images, or under bare walls that's the new way,' said the practical man who rubbed down John's horse after his daily ride.

She was also, of course, the daughter of a leading House in noble Scottish circles.

He had felt age and depression dropping off him like a moult as the visit ended. Brave warm blood coursed through his veins as he had not felt it for years, and hope was alive again. He would come back to Ochiltree ...

John Knox married Margaret Stewart a few months after that second visit to her home and if there were ever any other sketches of him drawn as colourful as that of Knox, the dandy going courting, they have been overlaid and buried, lost for ever, under a hundred tomes in black and white.

The piece which was the source of this uncharacteristic sketch of John Knox, was written about 1564 only a few years after the establishment of the Reformed Church. Roman Catholic dissenters were still free to write and circulate ribald essays and rhymes satirising the new Kirk and its founders in a way which would not have been tolerated later. In the old comment the writer suggests quite seriously that 'Johannes Knox interposed the power of his master the Devil' to prosper his wooing of Margaret Stewart by bewitching her. It gives a picture of the grave reformer which, love him or hate him, succeeding generations would not have recognised.

The Sad, Glad Tale of
Sir Arthur's Page

The old ballad that recites this story does not tell us what the crime was that outlawed Sir Arthur Nemo, laird of Cuninghame keep, but the tale begins on the morning when he stood on the seashore ready to take the rowing boat that would bear him out to the small ship lying at anchor in the bay, fitted and ready for his exile. His only companion was a page, pale, raven-haired and delicate, lately come to his castle and swearing to go faithfully with him into the wilderness, however far, and for nevermind how long. Sir Arthur had tried to dissuade him all the way from his castle.

'Go home, bonnie lad,' urged the laird, 'for your mother will be looking for you, and you've a good life ahead of you here in Scotland. There's no call for you to sail away, for you've folk at home that want you. I have none to weep for me and my going saddens no one.'

'The more you need a boy to bear you company,' replied the page, in the half-husky voice of near manhood.

'You must not come with me for you scarce know me, your time with me has been so short. But go instead and bear a letter for me to the love that loves me no more, the Lady Annie at Dunsallie Keep and take with it this jewel and the twist of my hair that's inside it, for a keepsake.'

'There are five bonnie daughters at Dunsallie, my lord. How shall I ken your love, the Lady Annie?'

'Oh you'll ken her lad, for she's the fairest and the most graceful with the brightest eyes, her hair is the colour of pale gold and her cheeks are like wild roses when she is happy, and fine white marble when she is wae.'

'Master, you must love her true,' sighed the romantic youth.

'If I were not out of favour with the King and at the horn for my foolish wilful ways she would be the wife of my heart and the lady of my hall. Now there's nothing for me but the sea and maybe a far country or a home on that fine ship. So I take your kindness, coming to give me good-bye. You're a good lad that might have been my squire. Fare you well then, Robin Goodheart,' and Sir Arthur turned and looked sadly towards the horizon.

The page doffed his feathered cap and with it came the tangle of raven ringlets so that now a halo of gold was round his head instead. Then he undid his lincoln green doublet and the white muslin of a lady's dress fell out and the page's figure stood there slim and lovely like a lily-of-the-valley blade.

'Have you another message I can take to your lady, Master?' 'he' asked gently.

Sir Arthur turned slowly at the sound of the softened voice and looked long and wonderingly at his lady, Annie, before he caught her round her slender waist.

'You've slept on the Big Hall floor this last sennight when I thought you bedded softly at Dunsallie and you've been at my side when I thought your back was turned on me.'

'Aye so,' she said happily and kissed him.

'I love you, Annie, but I cannot make an outlaw's bride of a gentle-reared daughter of Dunsallie.'

'I've not left comfort and kith to be sent back to them now, milord.'

'But I have nothing, save my boat.' She held out a hand bedecked now with gold and jewelled rings on every finger.

'I've enough here to buy a fleet of boats, if we will. You're at the horn here now, but the King is old and there will be a new one soon. Even so the world is wide and there's green lands there for Sir Arthur's bride. So hand me into the oarboat, my lord, and row me out to your sail.'

And the sun went down as the gloaming came and, though the Laird of Dunsallie was sad at the loss of his daughter, Sir Arthur and his bride stood on the 'Fair Winds' deck with their faces towards the west.

Lady Jean's Tapestry

There's fact in document and scrivener registers, with dates, signatures and oaths that claim to tell the whole truth of a matter. But sometimes there's another truth, that persists in the stories and songs of a place. And it would be a bold man who would say which truth was which.

The written chronicles have it that Lady Jean Hamilton married and lived in harmony with John, 6th Earl of Cassilis, until death parted them in the ripeness of time, that she was wistful when he was gone to the wars or on Kirk matters at Edinburgh; that she bore and reared him three children and that he mourned her earnestly when she died.

But the minstrel tales and ballads that have come down from the bards over the centuries tell different. And so, they say, does the tapestry that she stitched sadly in her later years and which moulders away somewhere in a kist at Culzean. And this story is from the tale that they tell.

Lady Jean was young, budding and beautiful the year her father, Thomas, Earl of Haddington began to seek out a well-coffered and titled husband for her. He loved his lass and would not have given her hand to an old man past his prime, however rich. Nevertheless she protested at some of his suggestions and laughed outright at others. Finally he thought to settle his choice on Lord Cassilis and sent for his daughter to urge her consent to his calling on the great Earl John.

Jean was a winsome girl whose singing and laughter filled the old stone pile at Haddington and she was a lass of spirit. Lord Cassilis was a little heavy-jowled, but a ruddy, well set-up figure of a man, and many a lass would have counted herself lucky to be his lady.

'Give me but today to think on it, Faither, and I'll give you my answer come evening.'

Alone in her chamber she pouted and sighed a little. Then, of a sudden, she tied a blue handkerchief, peasant-ways, on her fair head, kicked off her new French shoon and without squire or maid, set off to taste the delights of the fair-market a mile across the moor, a last fling for girlhood.

When she had made a round of the booths to see the mummers, the contorters and the Irish jingle-dancers, and bought a few ribbons for the maids at home, she was standing near a line of lasses, up for hire as serving wenches, watching an old woman pulling taffy. Jean looked healthy and bonnie and suddenly a florid man, taking her for a servant-lass, pinched her cheek so that her white teeth showed, as if he were examining horse-flesh. He took her small hand seeming to have no wish to let it go.

Just then a brown paw with strong lean fingers gripped the lustful hand of the farmer and Jean turned to see a handsome lad, dark as a wandering Egyptian, in blue sark and grey breeches, standing there.

'The lass is mine, sir. I've chased her across three shires. She'd be a bad bargain to you for she's a scald-tongued clip and lies abed half the day.'

The man growled and turned away to view the other wenches while the young man pulled a storm-eyed Jean by the elbow to scold her under a willow-tree at the edge of the green.

'You'd shouldnae talk with a man like that.'

Jean's anger melted, for the lad was doubtless a hired servant himself and only trying to save a decent girl from harm. Besides his eyes and mouth were humoursome and kind and she saw that he had an ancient fiddle slung across his back and, of all things, Jean dearly loved a fiddle tune.

They wandered together round the fair green for another hour or

more. He told her they called him Gipsy Johnny and that, for the present, he had work at a keep across the moor, and she told him that she worked in a Lord's castle a mile the other way. They were young, they were braw and in the way of man and maid they loved each other fine. He stole a kiss and she offered him another. He played a jig and a ballad to her on his fiddle and put a flower at her sash.

But Jeanie had to leave. She made some excuse to go and speak with a friend and when she was out of his sight she darted off among the booth lanes and away to Haddington.

He searched the fair until the last flares were doused and tipsy revellers tottered home. And he walked back to his place at the castle dejected that she had not been as smitten as he, for all the willing of her kisses.

And Jean was dejected too, for she could think of nothing but the lad who had squired her at the fair. Her father too, missed an expected show of spirit when he told her later that week that Lord Cassilis looked with favour on a match, providing that the dowry-tocher was right. She was silent and Earl Haddington sighed.

Jean considered bleakly. Doubtless if she was minded she could seek out that Gipsy Johnny, but she was not so lost to sensibility that she saw herself a stable-bothy wife. With the romantic certainty of seventeen she knew that she would never love another and if she could not be wed to the gipsy fiddler it did not much matter whom she took.

'Very well, Father. If so be Lord Cassilis is willing, he would maybe serve well enough.'

Her father went to work thankfully for he was coming on in years and it was high on his heart to see Jean wed before his time was done. The wedding date was set.

But there remained a few weeks yet before Jean would be off with her new lord to Cassilis and she spent them roaming the familiar fields and woods and walking by the bullrush and flag iris along the river. Mostly she walked alone, lost in dreams, but one evening she went with her brothers to dance jigs at a neighbouring keep. She rode on her cream palfrey, their way took them past the fair green where she had met Gipsy Johnny and she fell silent thinking of the laughing boy with the black dark head who had kissed her and won her heart. She patted the head of the palfrey and wished she could have seen the young man just once more.

92

She did see that black dark head again. She saw it that very evening, but it was above a fine broadcloth coat and a cherry silk neck-cloth and the eyes of young Sir John Faw of Dunbar were as shocked as hers when they met.

They danced that night and she went home all rapture and soft sighs and she did not feel, until the light of dawn broke cold, the pity of it all that she and John Faw had deceived each other when they met at the fair.

In the days that followed they met a time or two, by chance maybe, or maybe not, riding on the moors. They met at wakes and weddings and the gallant Sir John ran so counter to her betrothed lord in a dozen ways that Jean was as lost for love of him as he was of her.

She ventured once or twice to tell her father of her love for John Faw, but he would have none of it. He had higher ambitions for his daughter than marriage to the laird of a small fortalice, however handsome and dashing he was. He minded her sharply that Cassilis was a godly and earnest man, that she was pledged to him and that she was a fortunate maid to have found favour with him.

Before that summer had ended, Jean pale and drooping like a snowdrop, was wed to Earl John Cassilis of the stern face and wide lands of Carrick. He carried her home to his castle at Maybole where, in his own way, he meant to be a loyal and affectionate husband.

True to tell, he was no worse than dull and a mite narrow and Jean supposed that she was no harder off than any other woman who could not have the lad she loved. And when her husband was out seeing his herd or overseeing his tenants it seemed a harmless kind of faithlessness for her to mull over her little romance by starting to stitch the story of it into her canvas ... the willow tree, the ribbons, the blue sark and the fiddle.

But all Jean's dreaming served to keep her memories alive and vivid and, for all her lord's new wedded attentions and stolid kindness, she grew more forlorn and her sad looks palled a little on her husband. He took more often to his boar-hunting and falcons and to the business demanded of him by his stern allegiance to his purged kirk. But although he left her to the chilly passages at Cassilis by day, he did not neglect her bedchamber and in time she bore him three children.

Jean was most nearly happy in the time she spent with her children and, when not with them, in plying her crewel needle, putting memories of John Faw and happier days into her tapestry wool-work ... the white palfrey, the cherry neck-cloth and the sky-blue kerchief she had worn to the fair.

A kind of peace settled on her days and she raised her little ones tenderly and with affection. But their father was a strict man with the catechising and angry when his bairns stumbled their responses. It began to be whispered in the parish that all was not well at Cassilis, for its lady was blanch-faced and sad and she walked to and from the kirk of a Sabbath, with neither beck nor nod to anyone. And some, minding old clash from Haddington, said that she pined.

Maybe they said it too loudly and Gipsy Johnny heard of it far away in the lands round Dunbar, for one day in 1643 when Cassilis went off to represent the Presbyterian Kirk at the Assembly of Divines at Westminster the watchgate-man at Maybole let through a stranger. He was a gipsy-man with a gold earring and a yellow cloth on his head who said he was bid for minstrel work at some castle celebration for the master's homecoming. He said too that he had left his gipsy-band camped over the hill. The old gateman scarted his head at the puzzle of his dour master looking of a sudden for players, but as the gipsy jaunted his horse up the track to the entrance, the man put his feet on a bench in his gate-house and forgot all about the fellow.

Sitting at her window Jean caught the sound of a fiddle tuning somewhere below her in the yard. It was a wonder, for music had sparse place at Cassilis, but yet she did not move for the wild thought that sprang into her mind. Then there floated up to her one of the ballads Gipsy Johnny had played to her at the fair. Now she did look down and she saw far below her his dear face, and the bright warmth in it fade to concern at his sight of her pallid cheeks.

'I'm come to take you wi' me, Jeanie Cassilis,' he said simply, 'for yours is a bleak marriage that will not stand between me and my sweetheart.'

Her weariness and woe melted and, with tears in her eyes for her bairns, heedless of vows and reputation, she snatched up a shawl and ran down the cold stone staircase, out past the ancient Cassilis dule-tree and into the sunlit garden. There she was tenderly lifted to sit in front of Sir John Faw on his mare. They fled through the unused overgrown yett behind Cassilis and away into the woodland beyond, to join the troop of Faw men who, revelling in this 'gipsy' escapade, had come with their laird to steal away the Lady Jean.

If they thought to be too far from Maybole for capture by the time Lord Cassilis arrived home from London, they were luckless in that hope. The great meeting was over and those attending it dispersed to their own airts earlier than expected and, almost as the eloping lovers left the outskirts of Maybole, Lord Cassilis was cantering up to his own gate-house. Then he found noise and confusion in his court-yard, for Lady Jean's chamber had been found empty, confirming the wild tale of the mistress having been seen by a kitchen boy riding off with the gipsy minstrel.

'He cast a glammer ower her, Master,' stammered the steward, left in charge of all at Cassilis, when the laird was gone. Solemn Presbyterian though he was, John of Cassilis was a Kennedy, proud of his name and family and jealous of the honour now seeming to be besmirched. He called for a fresh horse and a troop of men, whipped the steward while he waited and then thundered after the runaways.

Not far to the south, at a place known ever afterwards as the Gipsy Steps, he came on the pair riding slowly behind the 'gipsy' band, kissing and cooing like the birds he fattened in his doo-cot, and without pausing to ask the whys and wherefores, he unhorsed Sir John Faw, cut him down and set his troop on the Faw attendants. Then he had his men take the captives back to Cassilis and, roughly catching up his wayward weeping wife, he followed the rest home more slowly.

Vengeance was swift and soon Sir John Faw and all his men dangled for the ravens from the Cassilis dule-tree, dead for con-spiring to make a cuckhold of the proud Kennedy who was his lover-lady's lord.

Jean saw them there as her hour for retribution came, when Cassilis took her, without silks or jewels but drab-garbed in a plain hodden dress, to the sturdy tower at the foot of the High Street of Maybole, there to bide until she died.

To keep her mindful of her wicked lapse, her husband had masons carve in stone round the windows of her prison room, the heads of gipsies, representing her lover and the blindly loyal men who had died because of her.

Over the rest of her days Lady Jean had but two pastimes. One was to look through her narrow windows over gardens of primrose, harebell, foxgloves and flower-shrubs in their season, when the clatter of hooves brought her children mounted on their lively ponies riding through the town. They came, laughing with their squire and

95

ladies, and remembering less and less of the woman in the ancient tower.

The other pastime was her sewing. When the Maybole street was empty of her children and mirk brought candle-light then she wove more of her sorry tale into the canvas, with herself seated on her lover's horse richly attired, with the arms of her John Faw round her. And as the years wore on, her wools grew dark and sombre as her thoughts, except for the red splash among them that was Gipsy Johnny's blood.

Over the centuries this story has been told with surprising certainty of its truth, although verifiable facts do not support it as it stands, nor does the very full *Historie of the Kennedys*. The dates do not tally with the facts. Jean died the year *before* the Assembly of Divines in 1643, to which her husband was supposed, in the story, to have gone. So if the elopement took place at all it was not in that year. Also there exist letters in terms of affection and endearment written by the Earl at his wife's death to various friends and relatives, though these could have been conventional expressions of grief in bereavement.

The earliest ballad telling the tale does not refer to Lady Cassilis by name, but does mention the Castle yett' (gate) a corruption of which could easily, over the ages, have become 'Cassilis yett'.

Honour would like to give Lady Jean's virtue the benefit of the confusion but sympathy and romance prefer the story.

The Beanscroft Devil

The small farm of Beanscroft lay in Fenwick, a thoroughly douce and godly parish, devoted absolutely to the Presbyterian cause in all its early stark and disciplined commitment. Nevertheless Fenwick, like parishes throughout Scotland, had its share of superstitious fear of unexplained happenings and, in the last years of the 18th century, Beanscroft farm was at the centre of gossip about haunted ongoings, and men and women talked of their fears with awe and chill fascination.

The farmer was a worthy man, regular in his work, family life and Kirk witness and it was said of him that he 'looked after his kye, sowed his corn, tilled his fields, stacked his harvest and was altogether fairly well-to-do.' He had a son to follow him who was ambitious further to improve the family lot. The lad had other interests too ... he versed a bit and sang, and he dabbled with chemistry in his small leisure, but he did not allow these cultural interests to interfere unduly with his duties on the farm.

The crofter himself (whom folklore does not name) was staunch to Kirk thinking and, although he had a vague secret belief in witches and bogles, he was convinced that as a worthy man he would not be disturbed by anything otherworldly. Indeed so sure was he, that he would never, until the end of his days, have admitted that he thought there *were* such things, if strange manifestations of unhuman presence had not begun to be noticed at Beanscroft.

They started simply enough as door openings and the rattling of shutters, things that could be put down to stiff winds. Even the tinkle of earthenware platters could be blamed on the cat. But when the furniture began to creak loudly in the night and the family was wakened by thumpings and moanings, and even a blood-churning scream echoing across the yard from time to time, the household lay abed limp with fear of bogles. There had never been such sounds and happenings at Beanscroft before. Every morning the family appeared for their brose with pinched, white lips, unslept eyes and faces drawn with fear.

The son was as sleepless as the others but he bravely offered to sit up for a night or two with his feet in a basin of water, for it was said by the herb-cure woman in the village that no kelpie would harm a human surrounded by water. Three nights he kept vigil while his parents and the terrified servant-child drew up the bedclothes over their frightened heads. But the lad saw nothing and said that only when he was back in bed did the unco' noises and rattlings begin again.

By the end of that autumn the spirits had become more wayward, the sobbing and groaning deeper, the cries more echoing and weird and the farmer's two workers had left him. The delft began to dance and crash to smithereens and, from the hastily lamp-lit windows, lights could be seen weaving in and out among barns and out-buildings, sometimes swinging wildly across the bothy door, some-times moving straight up and down as if rising and falling on some faery string. The farmer and his wife would stand rooted at their dormer window in their sleeping-shifts, gripping each other's hands until their knuckles were white . . . unable to call for their son for the strangle of fear in their throats. Then he would confess to having stood just as petrified at the other dormer-window, and when he announced that he was not willing to meddle with Satan at his night work again he was only echoing the certainty of all of them, that their tormentor was the Devil himself.

The farmer aged and grew daily more shrunken with the fear and worry of it all, and his poor wife ailed. The minister himself was called in and tried vainly to pray the Devil out of Beanscroft and to *read* it away, from the Book, where it told of the wicked spirits entering the swine and them careering to destruction over the cliff.

Now it happened that there lived in Kilmaurs a peasant philosopher called John Goudie, a freethinking man who was bold at proclaiming the conclusions he reached with all his meditation and thought. For some time he had been a friend of Robert Burns, but whether he took the philosophising smit from the poet or was Burns' friend because they had the gift in common, tradition does not tell. He was, however the talent had been acquired, independent of thought and defiant of speech and some thought him unorthodox, heretical and even dangerous.

He was not so far-gone a blasphemer to doubt God, but he certainly did not believe in a Devil who masqueraded as a lamp-swinging night-prowler, and he said so at the market, in the ale-house and even at the Kirk, when he deigned whiles to drop in there. He compounded his confident opinion by declaring also, that he had

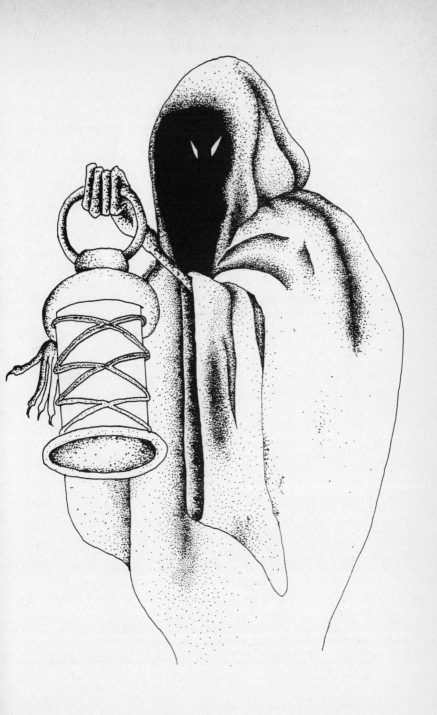

no doubt he could get to the root of the Beanscroft Devil mystery without tangling with Satan at all.

The last straw that broke the farmer's failing spirit fell at this stage of the matter when his cattle began to be found wandering loose every morning having been securely tethered the night before. There was no telling how they had been freed, for the ropes were obviously not cut, and yet by dawn, hung magically severed, the knots still tied round the tether-rings, the cows still attached to the other ends and trailing them about byre and yard.

Word of John Goudie's boast had by now reached the farmer and, at his wits' end, he invited the philosopher to come and lay his ghost.

As a God-fearing man and strict Presbyterian the farmer should, no doubt, have been hoping to show up Goudie as an unbeliever and fraud but, in fact, as a frightened old man with a craven son, he hoped more fervently that Goudie might really be able to better the bogle, chase him away, and bring peace to the farm. For in the deepest superstitions of his faint heart and in spite of his Calvinist rearing he truly believed that his steading *was* bewitched by Satan.

John Goudie arrived at Beanscroft with an unusual band of company for a half-atheist free-thinker. They were the Reverend Mr. Gillies of Kilmaurs and Mr. Robert Muir, merchant and Kirk-elder of Kilmarnock, though whether they were there to support John Goudie or to enjoy his discomfiture when he found himself helpless against the Devil, is not recorded.

Goudie questioned the farmer about rival neighbours who might bear him ill-will, or disgruntled workers about the bothy or kitchen, and even, when the mistress had gone ben the house, whether there might be a lady in the case with a jealous husband or sweetheart bearing him a grudge. The farmer was too wae to be incensed.

'No! No! No! No! he said to every question. Goudie prowled about the steading and came back smiling his tantalising philosophical free-thinking smile. He beckoned the farmer out and pointed to the severed tethering ropes.

'I didnae ken that Satan carried ackyfortis in his pooch.'

'Ackyfortis . . . ' repeated the farmer, thinking he was being joked.

'It's ackyfortis has eaten through your rope. Small wonder it doesnae show blade marks,' said Goudie drily.

'Well, he must carry it in his pooch, for he didnae find it here-aboots,' the farmer assured him.

'Maybe the De'il didnae, but the one maybe did that skirls and screeches and jingles your dishes, and that dances aboot your steading with his lamp. No, no, it's no' a speerit you're lookin' for here ... it's a pranking callant.'

Whether they doubted him or not, farmer, minister, merchant and thinker agreed to put the theory to the test. They would clash it about the parish that Goudie was flummoxed and then, since the moon would be full and bright, they would watch and see what happened that very same night.

Three of the four shivered as they took up look-out positions in the shadowy corners of the house and steading, but they sat out the hours bravely until the ghostly lamp came swinging slowly across the yard. The crofter stifled a yelp of fright at the sight of the devilish hand carrying the lamp and let his terrified eyes wander from the hand up the arm ... to the shoulder ... to the neck ... to the face ... of his son.

The farmer was the first of the four to move. He reached out with his walking-stick skelping the lad across the yard until it echoed with lustier howls than the Devil of Beanscroft himself had ever emitted. When the others saw father and son disappearing into the kitchen, the farmer seeming all at once to have shed his frailty and to be puffing with rage like a pouter pigeon, they nodded to each other and withdrew down the farm track. Not even seeing them go, the farmer pinned his lad to the gudeman's chair with the end of his ash and gave him such a lashing of the tongue as the old room had never heard before, even in the days when the farmer's wrathy old mother had been in her prime.

And as the son cringed before his furious sire he realised bleakly that it would be a long time yet before the old man reached the senility he had been trying so hard to hasten with his cantrips and that he would have a long wait yet for his inheritance. And they do say that in the days which followed the young man was such a laughing-stock that he fled the country and pursued his chemical experiments elsewhere, and that in time he had a fair success with them. But he never aped the Devil again as long as he lived.

The Little Tale of the Marauders of Kilmarnock

In the years when the Jacobite cause was simmering in other parts of Scotland, the south-west was largely uninterested in James, the King-over-the-water and his son, the darling Charlie. There was little intrusion into Ayrshire on their behalf and so a mild wave of excitement rippled over the town of Kilmarnock when a rumour spread that a party of Jacobites had raided Stewarton for supplies and was coming on to plunder Kilmarnock itself.

The town Drummer was sent out to patrol the streets and to give notice of a public meeting to devise ways for the citizens to protect themselves and their families, from what the town's leading men thought of as wild and savage highlandmen swarming over the civilised south..

The meeting took place and plans were made. A strong body of peaceable weavers and bonnet-makers was soon bravely playing soldiers armed with ancient swords, muskets, home-made spears and cudgels. A few rabble-rousers were rounded up to exhort the town army with slanderous shouts and speeches about sinful past on-goings by the mothers of Jacobites and the knavery and murderous wickedness of their sons. Fortified by the righteousness of their cause the townsfolk boldly set off to march in a body towards Stewarton. Back at home the womenfolk saw themselves as being probably under siege before nightfall and scurried about collecting everything they had of value, pewter, clothing, boots, plaids, money and food, and hiding it down their kailyard wells, under hedges or among the dangling thatch of their roofs.

Meantime the menfolk, with their carefully unearthed colours flying, their drums beating and their bonnets bobbing as they straggled in a brave unmilitary procession, passed through the town-centre, up by Soulis Street and Townheid. Half in dread, half in exultation, over the thought of the coming conflict they reached Craigsport where a snotty small boy thumbed a cheeky nose at them and told them it was 'a' lies'. A more reliable herd on an outfield pasture told them that the boy was right and the story but a hoax.

And so the brave citizens' army of Kilmarnock, with their drums and their colours, turned back. They mustered at The Cross, fired their muskets in the air and called for three cheers for King George.

In spite of not having had to face real blade thrust or shot fired in anger, for their willingness they were welcomed back with honour, and feted as heroes at Lucky Pinstoup's Howff.

But there was another, sadder story of the Stuart Rising and its link with Kilmarnock. And that was the tale of The Turncoat Earl.

The Turncoat Earl

The rout of Culloden was over. The blood of a thousand clansmen had seeped into Drumossie Moor. Other fugitives were being hacked down as they fled towards Inverness and the lochside beyond. Their leaders, who had been swiftly rounded up by Cumberland's lieutenants were now straggling despondently past the Hanoverian regiments as a line of escorted prisoners. Some were proud clan chiefs who had never known what subservience was, some were lowland lairds who, with their fathers before them, had been Jacobites over the fifty years since the last Stuart had been deposed, and had welcomed with high hearts each of three forlorn attempts to bring them back. Some were led by pure religious principles, some by a simple sense of fair play. But there was one man who was none of these.

He walked now in the drooping procession, his face haggard, his breeches torn and, without even the dignity of a covering on his head, his silver hair was dishevelled and wind-blown. As his part of the line of prisoners came abreast of one Hanoverian regiment which was watching them silently, a young ensign of Cumberland's army broke the disciplined rank of his company, took off his own bonnet and clapped it on the bare, beaten head of the enemy prisoner. Cumberland himself, who saw the action from the rear, turned away his head and neither then nor later ever reprimanded the breach of discipline. 'Butcher' though he was later labelled he had a glimmer of understanding for the gesture of the Hanoverian son to the Jacobite father, who was William, 4th Earl of Kilmarnock.

William Boyd had come by a long road to this bitter day, and there were those present who remembered that thirty years before, in 1715, the young William had been at the side of his father, the 3rd Earl of Kilmarnock at a muster in Ayrshire to raise a troop of five hundred men to defend the crown for George I. The boy had been reared and educated as a King's man and in his own children's early days had raised them to the same loyalty. Now two sons were still faithful Hanoverians but William himself had turned his Kilmarnock coat and influenced a third son to the same course. Lord Boyd's was one of precious few Kilmarnock coats that were ever donned for the Pretenders, and he did not make his change of allegiance until the early days of the '45 itself. For that town was Hanoverian almost to a man and it was greatly puzzled that its lord should suddenly take the other side.

But ... take it he had. And to the Jacobites he was a most popular and wildly acclaimed defector, a real feather in Prince Charlie's bonnet. He was heaped with honours by the Prince and assured of position, power, glory and wealth, when the Stuarts came into their rightful inheritance. Fortune seemed to be smiling on William Boyd in these middle days of the rebellion, and he was on the crest of a wave of success and favour after his notable part in the battle of Falkirk. His lady too played host to the Prince and his companions before the battle and it seemed that the future was set fair for the Boyds of Kilmarnock.

And then came Culloden.

The battle was almost over and Boyd might have escaped when, in the confusion of fire and horse, he rode straight ahead to join what he thought was a division of the Jacobites to lead it into honourable retreat. But the Stuart division was in fact a Hanoverian troop and the Earl was taken prisoner.

Along with other rebels he was escorted south and sent to the Tower of London with Lord Balmerino and Lord Cromartie. There they were confined until the day of the Accusing in Westminster Hall. Three coaches took them from prison to public hearing and the headsman's axe, carried prominently in the last of these, was the symbol of the capital gravity of the charges against them.

At Westminster all three pled guilty and after this public appearance they were taken back to the Tower to prepare statements as to why they should not be sentenced. Two days later the procession set out again for Westminster Hall, this time the impending doom hanging over them symbolised by the bearing of the axe with its naked blade turned towards the three Jacobites.

At the hearing Lord Cromartie appealed for mercy for the sake of his affectionate and innocent wife, his eight children and unborn baby.

Lord Balmerino defiantly refused to appeal for mercy or to plead extenuating cause or circumstance. He was a loyal Jacobite and convinced of the rightness of the Stuart cause.

Lord Kilmarnock did plead for clemency in a lucid well-reasoned explanation of the change in the course of his loyalties. He told the assembly that he had been sired and raised by a faithful subject of the

Hanoverian Kings and that in his turn he too had nurtured his sons in the same mould and had, until less than a year before, been himself a sincere upholder of the present Crown. He claimed that although he had changed course he had never at any time tried to persuade anyone to follow him. He also denied heartily the charge that he gave any order at Culloden that no quarter should be given to Hanoverian prisoners taken at the battle (and he persisted in this denial to his dying hour). On the contrary, he said, he had personally tended some of the wounded and dying.

He admitted that he had seen his error in changing sides in the conflict and claimed that when he rode into the Hanoverian ranks towards the end of the battle, he was actually returning to his old loyalty. Silence in the Assembly greeted this incredible statement.

Now he pled for mercy but vowed that, if his sentence was 'death', he would spend his last hours praying to God for the preservation of the reigning House of Hanover.

The three Lords were sentenced to hanging, disembowelling and quartering and, in the days between sentence and death, Boyd and

Cromartie petitioned the King for mercy. Cromartie was pardoned, but Balmerino never recanted his support of the Jacobite cause and as he was about to die his call rang out from the scaffold, 'God Bless King James!'

William Boyd, Lord Kilmarnock, declared his support of the cause to have been a brief and foolish abberation in long years of otherwise loyal service to Hanover. He pointed out that he had raised three sons hoping they would be loyal to the Crown and that two of these had fought against Charles Edward at Culloden. *His* last blessing before execution was for King George.

The records concerning Lord Kilmarnock's imprisonment, trial, appeal and death are full, in the greatest detail and certainly authentic, but they do not answer the question which teased his contemporaries and tormented his close friends, as to what had brought about this incomprehensible betrayal of inherited and early loyalty to the Crown ... folklore and theory have compounded the truth.

Some said the root cause was that he had married a Roman Catholic wife whose own family had been staunchly Jacobite and that she had probably influenced her weak and spendthrift husband to embrace that cause too. For had she not played hostess to the Pretender and his lieutenants before and after the Battle of Falkirk?

But there were others, perhaps better informed, who knew that that had been but a reluctantly fulfilled social duty. They knew too that Lady Anne Boyd was not a Roman Catholic but Episcopalian, though her family had been Jacobite, and they thought it more likely that bitter memories of her own family, torn by the 1715 Rebellion, would cause her to oppose her husband's part in the Rising of 1745. They were also aware that her health was failing seriously and that, fond wife and mother as she was, she could never have encouraged her husband and sons to be at odds over the old Stuart cause. Letters found later between the Earl and his Lady bear out their interpretation that she had disagreed with her Lord's decision to fall in with the Rebellion and that he had had to defend that decision to her. And other correspondence shows that in the short time left to her after her husband's death Anne Boyd remained as heart-close to the two sons who had fought for Hanover at Culloden, as to her wayward lad Charles who had opposed them.

Hardheaded men believed then and since that William Boyd had been an opportunist and had judged that there would be great popular support for Charles Edward and that position, wealth and power would surely go to the Scottish gentry who had lent him most support.

He might have lived a long life of contentment without any greater position or wealth than he had as Earl of Kilmarnock. But he was a weak man and it was generally believed that he was tempted by the rewards that might come to him when the Stuarts came to the throne again. For it was common knowledge that he had led a dissolute and careless life, had squandered what inheritance he had and was, in fact, in great penury with huge gambling debts. That belief was reinforced by the loss to Lord Kilmarnock of most of his worldly goods in a fierce fire which had gutted his home at Dean Castle shortly before his defection. The family had seen their ancient oaken chairs and soft rush carpets, the cushions and upholstery of Flanders damask and the five great brazen chandeliers lying in a charred heap on the banquet-hall floor after that fire.

Now his desperate bid to refurbish his life through Jacobite favour had brought his honour, his marriage, his family life and his future, to similar ruin.

At 10.15 on the morning of 18th August 1746 the London Sheriffs went to the great doors of the Tower of London and knocked. The formalities with the Warder of the prisoners were thus opened.

'Who's there?' said the Warder.

'The Sheriffs of London Middlesex.'

'What do you want?'

'The bodies of William, Earl of Kilmarnock, and Arthur, Lord Balmerino.'

The men were taken to the place of execution where Kilmarnock adjusted his shirt and waistcoat collar, and put on a cap made from a damask napkin so that there would be no tangling of clothes and hair with the axe. (The sentence of hanging and quartering having been altered to beheading.) He had by now withdrawn the lie that he had thought to rejoin the army of Hanover when he rode towards it at Culloden in error, and here at the place of execution his blessing was for King George.

Balmerino spoke bravely once more of his loyalty to the Stuarts and followed William Boyd up the scaffold steps.

Three letters, written during his imprisonment, remain from the 4th Earl of Kilmarnock. One was to the public, repeating the explanation of his behaviour and reiterated his loyalty to King

George. Another was to his eldest son, giving advice to the young man, who had fought on the opposite side at Culloden, advice which he doubtless regretted bitterly not having followed himself. The letter also commended his mother to the young man's care and comfort and urged him to do wht he could to help that one of his younger twin brothers who, like their father, had been on the Jacobite side at Drumossie Moor. The third letter was one of devotion and farewell to his 'Nanny', Lady Anne Boyd.

That last letter seems to have brought little comfort to the wife and mother of such a divided house. For during the days of trial, confinement and bereavement she is said to have paced restlessly up and down in a shady avenue of trees later known as Lady's Walk. There she wandered, weeping and singing sad songs of lamentation, along the white pathway that curved like a winding shroud. And, before two full rounds of the seasons had turned on The Walk, Lady Anne Boyd was dead, at thirty-eight years old, of an old ailment compounded by shame and grief and loneliness.

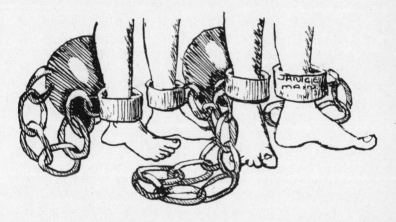

Many of the basic facts for this tale were gleaned from Miss Barbara Graham's scholarly treatise *Lowland Reaction to the '45 Rebellion*, and from the study of the Boyd family which is part of her research. Any inaccuracies are mine, not hers.

Auld Soulis

There were very few Jacobites in Kilmarnock aside from William Boyd, the 4th Earl, him they called 'Turncoat'. But there was another ... a town worthy who, if he had been bold and brave or had any kind of charisma to lead young hopefuls to follow him, might have roused the anger of the Hanoverian townsfolk. But he was no more than a wayward oddity and the people savoured him as something of a character rather than a threat. Living in a house next to the Soulis monument he was so generally referred to as Auld Soulis that very few citizens could have said with certainty what his real name was.

Auld Soulis then, followed the fortunes of the Jacobite army as closely as possible though he was dependent on some patient or humouring fellow-toper at Lucky Pinstoup's ale-house, to read tidings of them to him from a news-sheet. As often as not he was led wildly astray by some wag, wanting to see the triumph in his eyes, who told him that the Jacobites were already in Whitehall or that King James III had been measured for his crown. And to see him plunged into gloom, the same joker another night would tell him that the whole Jacobite army had taken to the Northern Sea in oarring boats. But sometimes the truth did get through to him and one of those occasions was a few days before the two armies were reckoned to be ready for a confrontation at Falkirk in the bitter January of 1746.

There was many a smile and titter rippled round Kilmarnock that day, when Auld Soulis, in his best cladding of sark, breeches and tattered plaid, clapped his Kilmarnock bonnet on his head and announced that he was for Falkirk to see the battle and maybe 'give the Highland gentlemen' the loan of his strong right arm. For that purpose he stuck an ancient pistol into the waist of his breeches.

Borne up by pride and good conscience he scarcely felt the first twenty-five miles of his trudge, but nonetheless fell into deep untroubled sleep on an attic chaff to the north of Glasgow. Next day with equal pride and good conscience, but chafed and blistered feet, he made slower progress. He was trying to keep his heart high with the thought of finding some decent inn in Falkirk with a braw smell from a soup pot, when he was accosted by a group of grim-faced Highlandmen, dark as gypsies, with unfriendly cudgels and muskets held menacingly close to his face. Auld Soulis was weak with fear and too petrified to reach for his grandfather's old pistol.

'Where is it you are from?'

When the towering leader of them spoke, Soulis felt the soft singing menace in his voice and was only too thankful that he was himself a bona fide Jacobite on the same side.

'Fae K... Kilmarnock,' he stammered.

'Who are you, Kilmarnock man and who do you serve?'

'I hae a letter for my lord the Earl of Kilmarnock wi' the Prince.' Soulis had no such letter and could but hope that either they would not search him or that they would believe a story that he had lost it. But they seemed little interested in his missive to William Boyd.

Another giant stepped from an alleyway, red-haired and bearded, and with a coarse sark lying open across a chest like an autumn forest. He had a dagger in his hand and gave the cue to the others to take theirs out also from their kilt waists. They pricked spots of blood from Auld Soulis's legs, arms and buttocks but doing him little real harm. All the same this brave Jacobite wished fervently that he had never left the safety of Hanoverian Kilmarnock.

Then one of the Highlanders laughed resoundingly, produced a bottle and lurched off. The rest put up their vicious little weapons and followed him hopefully into the shadows of a narrow vennel from the depth of which came the laughter of giggling girls.

Auld Soulis thankfully slipped into the first ale-house he saw and struck lucky there with a mat for the night and a jug of yill in the bar-room over which he heard clash of where the battle was like to be on the morrow.

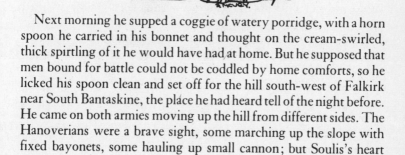

Next morning he supped a coggie of watery porridge, with a horn spoon he carried in his bonnet and thought on the cream-swirled, thick spirtling of it he would have had at home. But he supposed that men bound for battle could not be coddled by home comforts, so he licked his spoon clean and set off for the hill south-west of Falkirk near South Bantaskine, the place he had heard tell of the night before. He came on both armies moving up the hill from different sides. The Hanoverians were a brave sight, some marching up the slope with fixed bayonets, some hauling up small cannon; but Soulis's heart went out to tatterdemalion Highlanders racing them for the summit with their rough kilts kirtled up above their great bare knees. He skulked at the Jacobite rear, thinking to be more useful backing them up if the unthinkable happened and they retreated. Then when the front lines were a hundred yards apart there came the thunder of cannons, the scene was clouded and, through the smoke, came the sound of musket fire and later the clash of arms. Auld Soulis, who had never heard shot fired in anger in his life, stepped behind a boulder and swaddled his head with his plaid.

Then the rebel Highlanders uttered cries that curdled the blood, and through a tear in his plaid Soulis saw them rush on King George's army with broadsword and dagger, driving them down-hill, their feet stumbling and sucking in the mud. Auld Soulis crouched terrified behind his boulder gabbling a prayer that a late reinforcing party of rebels would not gather him up in the rush and bear him into the rout. But they all passed by safely, doing him no more harm than spattering his cladding with mud.

By now Auld Soulis wanted nothing so much as to be out of sight and earshot of the whole terrifying conflict. He took to his heels in the opposite direction from his heroes, his wind-lifted plaid flying out behind him, as he half-danced, half-scrambled his way towards the town.

He recovered himself there with a mull of hot ale in the howff and now that he was safe began to relish his adventures a little. He had no more money to pay for another night's lodging but he would linger here, taking a turn or two round the town between drinks, until he was put out. Then he would make for home where there would be a deal to tell the scoffers.

But he was not done yet with adventure for another tale to tell. About ten o'clock when the landlord jerked a thumb at him to leave, he stepped out shivering into the night and nearly collided with a torchlight party escorting a figure to the door of a lodging-house across the street. The man was tall and slender and a plaid fell to his ankles. His tousled hair shone fair under his bonnet in the torchlight and Soulis did not need to hear him addressed as 'Highness' to know that this was his Prince, victorious from the day's battle, not ten yards from him here in a Falkirk street . . . his braw Prince soon to lay siege to the old grey castle at Stirling and soon, said the old romantic heart of Soulis, to be Prince in London itself. Charles Edward stepped in under the door-lintel of his lodging and Soulis heard

112

shouting and laughter as the door shut him out into the darkness again.

The idea of setting off for home that night left Soulis like a cast cloak, for fear he might miss a second sight of the Prince in the morning. He skulked around the lanes and wynds till he found a crumbling cot rolled himself in his plaid and settled to sleep in the lee of its gable end.

He was rudely wakened in the cold light of morning by a jab in the ribs from a staff held in the hand of yesterday's red-haired soldier.

'Up with you, Lord Kilmarnock's lackey. There's work for you out there in the street.'

Auld Soulis blinked and rose to shaky feet pulling his muddy plaid behind him. He followed the Highlander into the street and was thrown the reins of a grey horse standing there with two wounded Jacobites slumped against each other on its back.

'The Prince's army marches north ... and we're to leave these men at Stirling. Take you the reins and fall-in with the marchers at the cross-tracks there.'

This was not to have been the way of it at all. Soulis could not have told that Stirling lay far to the north-west of Falkirk but fine he knew it wasn't on his way to Kilmarnock. All the same he saw the Highlander's dagger-hilt at his waist and stepped forward with the reins to go and find the rest of the army as it mustered outside the town.

At first he walked the horse in the midst of the troop of men but then he slowed a little and let them overtake him on each side, until he was in the loose rear ranks and finally straggling behind them altogether. Then they came to a bend in the road, he gave the horse a slap on the buttock, left the dazed and wounded Highlanders to the common-sense and obedience of the horse to follow the army, and himself jouked behind a gorse-hummock.

He crouched there until he was cramped, and then doubled back, skirting Falkirk and set out at a fast lick towards home. He had one night in a comfortable barn north of Glasgow town and the next in the draughty doorway of a Kirk. Then thankfully he was home.

His active service to his Prince now over, Auld Soulis embroidered his small adventures at Falkirk into a rare exploit of daring and gallantry so that those in Kilmarnock who were entertained for the next twenty-five years by his stories (and plied him well to tell his tales) never knew at all what was the truth of them.

113

The Laird of Changue

Many a tale they tell among the Barr hills, of the wilful Laird of Changue, who was a notorious smuggler of his day, a high-liver, spendthrift, careless, swaggering and bold. But none of the stories chills the blood like the telling of how he twice met the Devil himself. The first of these confrontations took place once after the Kirkdamie Fair, where the hailfellow laird was a kenspeckle figure every time it was held, as indeed he was at all such events in the lands of Carrick.

The mountainous country there ranges over many miles of Ayrshire. It is riven by valleys carrying the tumbling burns which provide water for its famed illicit stills and shelter the tiny gold-crest finches that flutter among the larch trees growing there. Since unrecorded times shepherds in these hills have trailed the sheepwalks and later seen the tiny saplings, planted to provide windbreak, grow into the tall trees that temper storms to the small settlements and villages in its folds.

Kirkdamie Fair traditionally began in the morning with the legitimate trading of sheep, the buying, selling and bartering of wool and the laying-in of stores by cot-house wives who might be storm bound in the wintertime when the hills were shawled in white. It would finish at night with groups of mellow men sitting round tables where lads sold the spirits stilled secretly in the hollows by the Carrick burns. Or sometimes fiddlers and pipers tuned up for the dancing on the green sward in the midst of the fair. During the day, between start and finish, there were ribbon booths and farl stands to patronise, and round the field bairns gawped at the jugglers and cheered the staff-pole champions; youths, watching men grappling and throwing each other, boasted that they could outwrestle the professionals. But in their hearts they knew that only one man among them could truly do that, and that was the Laird of Changue. He was tall and fearless and ready to master any unwary outland performer who threw out a challenge.

His feats of strength and hard gambling were the talk of the echoing hills, girls and gudwives swooned for him and men saluted one who could greet alternate wealth and poverty with equal spirit.

At the time of this story the Laird of Changue strode across the slopes to Kirkdamie well aware that he was 'rupt' of all his money and much of his kind. His very chickens ailed, his goats were dry, his apple-trees gone barren, his pigs diseased at mouth and foot and although he was never a man for gloom, he did meditate as he climbed on how best to retrieve the situation.

He met friends at Kirkdamie Fair and although his affairs were at such a sorry pass he bantered and guffawed with them as if he had never a care in the world. He made them laugh as they plied him with the rough liquor from the stills. He had a strong stomach for spirits and the more he took the better and bawdier grew his tales. All afternoon Changue caroused with this one and that and by darkfall was tacking home across the hills so that he trebled the long path to Changue, and had to rest by a scatter of boulders on the way. And there he fell into a dozing sleep.

Without the support or audience of his dramming cronies the Laird's problems gave him stark and unpleasant dreams and when he was roused by a strange sensation that he was caught in a halo of heat and light, he shifted uncomfortably feeling that he was only half-awake. From this warm glow around him he heard beguiling, caressing words, sweet as the dripping of honey, offering him ease from his woes for the rest of his life. The price was small, purred the voice and need not be paid for half a lifetime of years yet.

'What price?' asked the spell-bound Changue, characteristically thinking only for the moment, letting the future take care of itself and scarcely wondering if he would ever be able to pay the cost of such ease.

'Nothing that you cannot spare,' crooned the soothing voice.

'But what?' asked the Laird, but incuriously.

'No more than your soul when you die.'

'You want my soul?' intoned the Laird, all sense suspended.

'No, no,' soothed the voice, 'only the promise of it now.'

It was a promise easily given in that twilight spirit world outside Kirkdamie, when he was young and hale and not to be presented with the bill of account until old age and death.

Then the warmth faded and the night grew chill. Laird Changue awoke sobered and cold but lightheartedly comforted that his dream might token better times ahead.

And so it seemed. For soon his fowl laid eggs enough for a dozen families, his apple-trees were miracles of blossom in spring and laden with fruit in late summer. His pigs grew sonsy and healthy and his goats' milk was rich and brimmed the pails. His smuggling was lucrative and undetected, his investments successful and secure and his barns were full.

After a reasonable spell of prosperous life that none of his roistering and gaming seemed to drain, but nevertheless before he considered himself ripe with age, the laird took a delirium fever that had his doctors shaking their heads and his nephew-heirs sigh sadly (but dust their strongboxes ready for his passing). The delirium left him and it was thought he was near his end and having a last lucid period before weakness overcame him. It was then that the Devil of the Kirkdamie meeting came again to Laird Changue and told him that his time had come, and that he would meet him shortly in a clearing in his orchard and exact his due.

But the Laird of Changue thought otherwise. He gathered all the remnants of his strength, left his sickbed and, grasping his sword from its place on the wall, went to the orchard at the appointed time to meet his Devil creditor. At this meeting there was no warm rosy cloud. The Devil stood there all too plain with his cloven hooves, the sting in his tail, the horns on his head and his two great wings. Before Satan began his spiel Changue drew a circle with his sword point and took an oath that if his adversary could put him outwith the ring he could have his black way and carry him off to Hell. But if not then the Devil must cancel his debt.

And so battle commenced. The Devil tried with all his might to kick Changue out of the circle but the Laird struck at his cloven foot so that the natural slit was deepened by several inches. Infuriated he tried then to stab the Laird with the deadly sting in his tail, both knowing that, if it entered, then Changue would die and fall outwith the circle. But the laird slashed the tail with his sword and the sting fell out of it to the ground.

Now Satan turned on him the venomous head horns to gore him to death across the circle line, but Changue's blade struck them off the Devil's head and they flew high, wide and out of the ring.

Then the Devil, certain of his last weapon spread out his two expansive wings to rise over Changue, crush him to the ground, then lift him out of the holy circle. But in spite of his weakness all the swift skill the Laird had learned from his years of practice at Kirkdamie Fair, came to his hand now and, before the wings lifted up the Devil, Changue's sword flashed down on the base joint of the wings so that they were severed from the villain's back and he was sent spinning from the circle and lost his battle for the Laird of Changue's soul.

The Elders who Forgot Themselves

On the Kirk Session of one of the congregations of Ayr were two particularly upright and much respected men. One was the Bailie Saunders, bien leader of society and pillar of the Kirk, sometimes taking the pulpit and the prayer-meeting when the minister was from home conducting a service at a neighbouring Kirk. The other was Mister Erchie Williams who, although a publican, was himself totally abstemious and wont to give wise counsel and timely warning to unwise topers on his premises (even as he slipped their coins into his takings drawer). He too was considered, and considered himself to be, a godly man, generous to widows and orphans, and was in the top half-dozen on any local charity subscription list.

Their session, like the rest in Ayr, spoke out firmly against the usual sins of public brawling, drunkenness, free love and Sabbath breaking. But for some reason it set its communal face against theatrical performances even more than these other wickednesses and, never in its wildest or most gloomy predictions of the ill that could come of play-acting or dancing, did it expect to have to charge one of its own elders with having attended at a theatre. Play-going in Bailie Saunders' philosophy was next kin to murder, as he supposed it to be in Mister Erchie Williams' also.

Now there came to the sinful city of Glasgow in the Bailie's prime-time of life an actor, of wide fame in London for his romantic good looks and his great art, and provincial unworthies were greatly excited when he was to make a nation-wide tour. In the course of it he was billed to appear at the Theatre Royal in Dunlop Street, Glasgow.

It chanced that very week that, unknown to each other, the Bailie and Mister Williams were both in the city on business.

Curiosity about the depravity of the actor's hero-worshippers and, he told himself righteously, a wish to see the evil blasphemy at its roots the better to fight it, led the good Bailie to go and take a look at the crowd jostling round the theatre door. He might have been better to do this from the other side of the street because, when the doors were opened, he was swept forward and inside along with the eager and impatient audience.

He was mortified but with resignation he took this as God's will that he was to examine the performance and judge its ongoings from

117

personal experience. ˙And so, through gritted teeth, he asked for a seat-ticket for the centre of the stalls.

But ah!... the wages of sin ... Bailie Saunders began by glowering at the gilding and plush, the lights, the painted scenery and, worse, the painted theatrical women ... but gradually and insidiously the play began to grip him and he warmed to the story (and it has to be said that in the plot Good was slowly but certainly triumphing over Evil). By the end of the piece Bailie Saunders was standing up clapping and cheering as loudly as anyone in the theatre when the clean-cut and handsome actor gallantly handed forward his sweet little leading lady, for applause.

By next day the glow had subsided and the Bailie knew that he had been seduced and carried away on the very wave of emotion that good men knew played havoc with a man's morals. He would not, however, compound his misery by confessing such a fall from grace to anyone and adding to his shame by having it common clash.

By the next week, though, there was a persistent rumour round. Ayr that one of its upright citizens, a Kirk elder, had been seen entering a housing of entertainment in Glasgow. Bailie Saunders sweated and grew cold by turns and there was still shame and uneasiness in his relief when he heard it was Mister Erchie Williams who was being named as the sinner. His discomfort grew worse when the Session Meeting was called, without Mister Williams, to discuss the matter. Saunders went.

118

The elders found it so hard to believe in Erchie Williams' crime that they decided a discreet call must be made on him to probe gently the possibility that he could so far have forgotten himself. The good men's choice to broach the delicate matter fell, to his horror, on Bailie Saunders as their leading light.

'A fearful charge against you is this Erchie,' said the Bailie with a grey, troubled face. 'It cannae be true,' he added with pious sadness.

'You think no?' said Erchie. Then he eyed Saunders for a moment in silence. At last he went on to say that 'yes' he had gone to Glasgow and 'yes' he had taken a dander in Dunlop Street, and there he'd seen an old friend struggling to get into the theatre with the crowd. Curious, he had followed him in, but had only managed, himself, to get a seat in the gallery.

'. . . the gods' them play-goin' sinners call it, you ken.' He did not see the stage too well from up there but he had a rare view of the audience. And 'och dearie' but it had been fairly carried away with itself . . . especially one white-thatched man in the stalls . . .' a man, no unlike yourself Bailie . . .' a noble looking fellow for all his sins, who seemed to be leading the cheering and shouting.

The Bailie's bubble was burst and the two confessed all to each other, each well understanding the worthy motives that had prompted the other to find out the truth about the play-acting. Both were agreed too that these motives would not be understood by their Brethren and that it would be folly to explain. But the Session did await Bailie Saunders' report.

'Never fear, I'll think on something to say to the Session,' he promised Erchie Williams.

' . . . Gentlemen,' he said when the time came, 'I can tell you only that you can trust Mister Williams' word as you can trust my own, and that he would no more have done such a thing than I would myself . . . that his soul is as white on the matter as my own.'

General relief and thankfulness greeted this report for, although they were strict men, they were Brethren and had no wish to discover one of their number in such a grievous fault.

It would be comfortable to record that the two sinners were wise enough to let the matter rest there and leave their fellow-elders in happy ignorance of the truth. But it is said that after a sleepless night they made full confession to the minister and left him wishing heartily that they had kept their guilty secret to themselves.

C. ULLRICH

The Wit and Wile of Alexander the Dagger

It was late autumn of the year 1394, an autumn of mellow mists shrouding the contours of the Ayrshire hills, and it was growing snell for even the hardy Alschunder Dalgour (Alexander the Dagger) to be fugitive from the wrath of his superior, Lord Douglas of Wigtown.

Alschunder had been at odds with authority since some heedless visitor at his father's home years before had given the lively corn-haired laddie a fine silver dagger, chased with Spanish scrolls and whorls and honed to a sharpness that gave the steering boy a sense of invincible confidence in his fighting powers. No matter that in young manhood he was 'at the horn', outlawed, for more of his life than he had been respectable, he loved the open moor life and the outwitting of Douglas's troopers doggedly set to catching him. He was younger son to a younger son and had no property to defend, no fortune to gamble and, until he was a man in his thirties, had been content to be his own judge and lawman.

But that summer just past he had met the fair Lady Alicia at the castle of a friend who was sheltering him. She had spoken modestly but wittily in the small company and he had seen her blue eyes follow him with flattering constancy. Then word had come that he was once again only half a day ahead of Lord Douglas's hunting men and he had had to take to the hills again. Alicia had not drawn away her hand when he kissed it and there had been a heart-turning sadness in her smile as she watched him go.

Now his jaunting moorland life had begun to seem empty and worthless, when he laid it in mind alongside a modest keep some-where with the golden-haired Alicia sitting by a warm ingle with her needlework and maybe rocking a cradle with her foot, and himself on the other side the fireplace with his accounting book tallying out his small wealth in hardy cattle, grazing goats, a hill of sheep perhaps, even a little ship at sea, cargoed with spice and silk.

It was a tempting picture. But he had no keep, no cattle, no sheep, no spices or silk. He was a wanderer, always just ahead of capture, and his bold free life held less and less charm for him as that autumn slipped into chilly winter, and he happed his grey plaid closer round the hilt of his silver dagger.

December came and Yule drew on. Now he had run an officer of Douglas's troop out of the village of Kilmaurs at the end of his dagger in a quarrel over an insult to his mother. And he was on the run again. He flitted about the countryside, with a night, once in a while, in the guest chamber of a kindly friend, bold as ever in the company of old acquaintances but dowy-sad when he watched their wives and bairns, ate at cheerful tables and saw the bright, woman-worked tapestries on their walls.

Then three days before Christmas he heard two pieces of gossip at an inn near Stewarton, that chivvied him into action. One was that some knight with a fancy French name was said to be paying court to young Lady Alicia and second that Lord Douglas Wigtown, ex-asperated by renewed tales of Alexander Dagger's rebel ways, had made a declaration that 'Whosoever shall bring me the head of Alschunder Dalgour will be given in reward, lands in Stewarton of Cuninghame valued at forty merks'.

Alexander considered. First he slipped into Kilmarnock to see a lawyer. Then before sun-up and after nightfall he rode round the homes of those who sheltered him when he was in need and gathered from them a small retinue. As fearless as a King's favourite he rode through Ayrshire into Wigtown and on the morning of Yule day arrived at the town while the Earl Douglas was at mass.

At the sound of clattering hooves outside the chapel, Lord Douglas rose from his knees. Then he heard the heavy doors being pushed open across the echoing flags and turned in the gloom of the old chapel to see Alschunder Dalgour standing in the nave with the hilt of the silver dagger held out towards his overlord in one hand, while in the other were deed-documents prepared by the lawyer in Kilmarnock.

'My Lord,' began Alexander, 'you have offered this forty-merk land to anyone that would bring you my head. There is none so meet as myself to do this thing. I herewith bring my head, attached to my body, and desire your Lordship to keep faith with me as you would with any other.'

The Earl was a bold man himself, a fair man too and one who had a vein of humour in his make-up that responded to this effrontery. It might be, he thought too, that the responsibility of land, and of family life if he took to it, would tame young Dalgour better than a host of fighting men.

'You leave me no choice, Alexander Dagger, for well I see you've brought a head with you that's full of wiles and rough wisdom ... Your papers, if you please sir!' Douglas examined them on a stone wall-seat and had two of the chapel priests look over them too and when Alschunder had kicked his heels for half an hour the scrolls were undersigned and handed back to him.

With words of warning for future peaceable conduct and of guarded pardon ringing in his unscathed ears the rebel leapt up on his mount and made off for Stewarton to claim his estates. Then he offered them in marriage to Lady Alicia before she could give her hand to the fancy French titled Lord. Tradition does not tell whether she accepted him but it *is* said that in time Alschunder and the Earl of Douglas became close friends.

Archie Mc.Lintock's Visit to Hell

Archie Mc.Lintock was a decent enough man, quiet and steady in his ways mostly, but given, from time to time, to taking a dram or two, or maybe three, too much. It seemed to him a trifling fault for his wife Kirsty to scold him about.

'Satan aye waits for them as takes to drink,' she would chawner at him every time he fell to temptation.

It was the only rub in an otherwise good marriage for Kirsty was a blithe wee body that turned the lightest girdle scone in Galston and had the triggest kitchen, with a stone jar of hedgerow flowers and grasses always on the sill of their cottage winnock, even in winter.

And this was winter. It was in fact Hogmanay and market day at Kilmarnock. Archie went as usual with his nag and cart to sell some of the small produce of his farm. Kirsty saw him off as usual, with her dire warning about Satan ringing in his ears. He did a sober round or two of the stalls after his business was done and then he met a friend from Mauchline that he had not seen since last market day. They went to the old Wheatsheaf to crack, and sat out the rest of the afternoon there, over dram after dram, until there was precious little left of the takings of either of them. Archie never knew how his friend left Kilmarnock and scarcely how he did himself.

He was lifted into his cart and since he insisted that he was quite capable of driving home himself, over the river and up the road to Galston, his fellow-drinkers (faced with a hard enough job to get themselves home) took him at his word, slapped his smart little mare on the rump and started her up through Crookedholm at a fair lick. She knew the way home as well as any other habitant and was soon trotting up the miles with Archie half-lying half-sitting, the reins loose in his hands.

Near the coal-pit he woke up briefly and struggled to his feet to take the cart 'chariot-style' and make a dramatic entrance to the main street, but he lurched and toppled out on to the ground where he lay, now stunned as well as drunk, while the mare, unaware that she had lost her driver, ambled on.

The year's last night shift was just going on and half-a-dozen of the miners found the 'body' as they turned towards the pit. One of them lifted his lamp to look at the face.

'It's Archie Mc.Lintock, up to the bung wi' drink,' he said. There was a whispered consultation. The minister, passing by from a night call and seeing them, thought they were acting the Good Samaritan to Archie to take him home, and that it would be a kindness on this Hogmanay night, to play the priest who passed by, and not bother to tale-tell on the sinner to his Kirk Session.

The voices murmured on and he missed the guffaw that rose when he turned in at the manse yett.

Archie, still senseless from his pickling and tumble, was lifted on to a hefty shoulder and carried limp to the pit-head and into the cage waiting to take the new shift down. At the bottom they bore him carefully along to a corner of the pit where jutting crags of unhewn coal hung menacingly over the tunnel. There Archie was laid tenderly to sleep off his drenching.

Around midnight he came to a bleary clarity and half opened an eye in his thick throbbing skull. He had never been down the pit before and would not have recognised it even in full possession of his senses. He had certainly no idea where he was now. Through his dwam, a huge figure slotted in and out of focus with twelve great smoking haloes of light around its head, and eyes of startling whiteness in a black and wicked face. A wide cloak hung majestically from its shoulders and in its left hand it held a gutttering torch for a sceptre. Archie saw in the guise neither pit-lamp nor coal-dust, horse-rug nor lighted hempen and straw cords. He saw, as he was meant to see and as Kirsty's righteous voice had so often warned him he would someday see, Satan 'waiting for them as takes to drink'. Now he knew for certain that Satan had come for him.

Archie sat up, too terrified even to lay his aching head againt a ridge on the coal-face. The Devil advanced towards him and he shrank back. The Devil stopped and drew himself up with immense dignity.

'Archie Mc.Lintock, late of the Parish of Galston ... ' When he heard the awful word 'late' Archie would have covered his ears if he had had the strength ... but now the voice was droning on ...

'I, Laird of the Underworld, have waited your arrival here since The Year of the Frosted Harvest ... ' Archie minded fine that that was the year he was first carried home insensible to his frightened bride.

'How came I to be in such a place, for I was hale and strong at the Kilmarnock market the day?' he quavered.

'You died drunk, Archie Mc.Lintock, so where else was there for you to go? You didnae think surely to get following innocent bairns and sweet virgins, and godly old men?' And unearthly laughter echoed from the dark infernal cave that lay behind Satan.

'I suppose no'', said Archie humbly, 'but in my right mind I'm a God-fearing man that was baptised and wed in the Kirk.' Then he thought on Kirsty and the fear chilled him that his well-doing wee wife would never join him here and that, if he was to stay, that would be them parted for ever.

'Is there no hope for me to make my stay here short?' He did not want to offend the Devil by finding fault with the hospitality, so he spoke timidly.

'The usual's not far short on a thousand years,' said the black creature doubtfully.

'Lord, Lord help me. I'll no even ken Kirsty by sight then!' groaned Archie. 'Ocht I wish I'd never even lipped the whisky ... is there no' some bargain I could make wi' you milord?' Archie hoped this was the correct way to address so mighty-looking a personage.

'You could maybe slip out before your name was on the register, back into life for a year or two yet, if you were to promise never to touch the drink again, for we dinnae want teetotalling saints here.' there was a weird echo of assent from what Archie now thought of, and remembered afterwards, as being the Spirits of Hell among the shadows. And he was in no state to wonder whether renewed life would be tolerable without a dram from time to time.

'Aye, aye ... I would be pleased to take an oath on that,' he declared eagerly.

'Well, first you must drink a Devil's potion to your promise from my silver cup, then we'll see if you can be got back to where you belong.' And the Devil kirtled up his cloak and brought out what Archie knew must be a Satanic vessel, though now his head was clearing a mite, it looked uncommonly like a tin flask.

'Drink!' commanded the Devil concerned that the prank would fall flat and the cure fail, if Archie sobered up too soon ... and also that half the shift would be gone with nary a lump of coal cut. He swung the hemp torch in a great figure of eight, just clearing the tip of Archie's nose and singeing the shoulder of his jacket.

'Drink!' he repeated, and the crofter hastily took the flask, steeling himself against an infusion of brimstone and infernal herbs. Nevertheless he quaffed bravely and was agreeably surprised to find it tasting not unlike Nancy Paton's brandy.

125

But as he took it in one long swig on top of his earlier imbibing, he did not have time or wit to analyse it further before he was laid out cold again under the flickering pit lamps. And so he remained until the shift ended. Then he was hoisted to the surface again and carried home to Kirsty.

Archie woke to find himself alive and safe in his own bed and later, although he entertained all-comers at Nancy Paton's howff and at the Kilmarnock Wheatsheaf to the dream-story of his meeting with Auld Nick among the dark shadows and flickering fires of Hell, his own laughter was uneasy, for he was never just quite certain that it had been only a dream. Was the smell of the brimstone not still in his nostrils and that faint scorch mark not still on his market jacket?

It would make a neat and worthy ending to record that Archie Mc.Lintock never touched another drop. But it would not be true. All the same he never took two the same night, or risked the chance that if ever he found himself in the nether region again, he would not be able to bargain himself out of it so easily.

He took a second notion to Kirsty too, minding the fright he had had when he thought never to see her winsome face again, or at least not until it was a thousand years older.

126

Rowallan

A Scottish chief of long ago is said to have been sailing at his leisure in a long oar-boat along the Ayrshire coast. All was serene and he bade his lead boatman, Allan of Stewarton, take him farther out into the

bay so that he might better see the hinterland hills. The boatmen were skilled, the evening seemed settled and the boat drew out far from the shore.

Then across the gentle sky there rolled a surge of sullen cloud, grey on grey. And, as suddenly as it later died, a great storm broke and began to play havoc with the oars. The boat heaved and fell in the boiling sea and all seemed lost. The Chieftain, a brave enough man in battle, was afraid on this unkindly sea and his voice wavered as he pleaded with his leading oarsman.

'Row, Allan row! Bear us safely to land and if you save us I'll grant you lands on Carmelside, rich lands with siller to build you a keep. Hill and valley and rivers of fish will be yours . . . but just row, Allan, row!'

Allan urged on the others and bent his own back to the oars and against the whetting wind. Eventually exhausted but triumphant they reached shore safely. Allan won his prize. The castle and lands on the bank of the River Carmel were his and in minding of the adventure that brought him to his estate he called it by the name, 'Rowallan'.

The same story is told in a poem by George Paxton of the neighbouring village of Kilmaurs:

> A Scottish Chief in days of old,
> As hoary headed sires have told,
> Was tossed upon the main
> Small was his skiff, the tempest blew
> The trembling Chieftain urged the crew
> The distant shore to gain.
>
> 'Row, Allan, row', the baron cried
> High on the foaming surges ride
> And bear me safe to shore
> A rich domain at Carmel-side
> Oe'r hill and dale extending wide
> Is thine for evermore.'
>
> The quivering oar bold Allan stretched
> The solid land the baron reached
> And Allan won the prize . . .
> Adorned with ropes of twisted stone*
> Long on thy banks Rowallan blown
> But still the storm defies.

* Presumably a design on Rowallan Castle stonework.

128

A Roof
of their Own

Long long ago the wild moorland of South Ayrshire was the kingdom of the gipsy people and was known in these parts as Little Egypt. Among the folk who wandered there and among the villages on its fringes was an ageing gipsy couple.

Wed by habit and repute and a brief gipsy ceremony in Galloway they had seen each other through joy and hardship under the open sky for fifty years together. Their sons were wild gipsy rovers, long since off their hands, and they themselves were beginning to feel the winter winds snell and sear. The Hungry 1690s were closing and there were times when the old woman would look enviously at some of the sturdy cots they passed. Then she would complain to her husband that she was getting too old to sleep in the lee of walls or to slip secretly in beside animals in the dark when the cot-folk behind the room wall were asleep ... that an old pair like them needed a thatch over their heads.

One day during the last bitter winter of that cruel decade the two were selling their trifles at a cottage in a valley farmtoun where they were kenspeckle figures most years. They were showing the farm-wife their horn spoons and blackjack toffee when the minister called to ask after the family, and all three visitors were invited to pull in at the table for a companionable dish of salted herrings, a rare treat in famine time. There was crack of the vicious weather and the way it had culled the valleys of the bairns and the sickly and the aged, and the gipsy woman lamented again that she and her man had no place of their own.

129

'There's an old cot down there by the burn below Langriggs,' said the minister. 'The folk there lost their babies of the famine sickness and they're gone away to the south to look for better fortune elsewheres. It's not much, mind, but it would be shelter and I can let you have it, for it's at my disposal. That's if you're set on having a place.'

They moved in before the winter clenched its hardest. The old man made two chairs and a table, and the wife sang a cracked gipsy song as she filled a chaff bed and put it down, dry and wind-free. They set the ingle roaring up towards the lum-hole, put out platters beside it for their brose and rubbed their hands before the flames. And they thought they were the happiest couple in the whole of Little Egypt.

Three weeks later the old woman said suddenly, 'Husband, I'm missing the scud of the clouds and the glimmer of the stars and the streaming of the moonlight in here where it's so dark.'

And so the next day the man took the door off the house and left a space there, the better to see the moving sky.

The next night the old gipsy wife said, 'Husband I'm missing the song of the mavis and the cries of the peasweep and the whaup, here behind the walls.'

And so the next day he cut away a corner of the dangling turf roof and let a great hole into the cot, the better to hear the birds.

A third night the old gipsy wife said to her man, 'Husband, now I can see the scud of the clouds and the stream of the moon's light, but I'm soon to be missing the scent of the heather and the wild flowers of the open moors.'

And so next day the little old gipsyman crashed his peat-spade through the shutter across the window chink the better to smell the heather and the flowers of the open moors when the softer weather came.

The fourth night the old woman said, 'Husband, I have the skies and the birds and the scents coming, but I'm missing the wind and the rain in my face.'

And so next day the old man put water on the ingle till it hissed on the firestones. He emptied the chaff from their pallet on the wind, and strung their pots and pans and other peddle-wares over their shoulders. He propped the door back into the door space behind them, and they took to the sheep-tracks and the open skies of Little Egypt again.

130

The Shaming of Lady Flora Hastings

It was just after Christmas of the year 1838 that Lady Flora Hastings began to feel unwell. She was a quiet, thoughtful young woman, recently appointed a Lady of the Bedchamber to the young Queen's mother, that somewhat foolish woman, the Duchess of Kent.

Lady Flora was the eldest daughter of Viscount Loudon and had been born and reared at Loudon Castle near Galston. She was sensitive and, in her free time at court, enjoyed walking in Buckingham Palace gardens or sitting writing poetry in her own sitting-room.

Her fatigue and discomfort persisted into the New Year of 1839 and she consulted one of the Queen's physicians, Sir James Clark, who began a course of treatment for the illness that he suspected.

Neither tradition nor factual report tells how the first rumours began to be murmured at court, but first one corner then another buzzed with innuendo and outright claim that the unwed Lady Flora Elizabeth Hastings was with child. Soon the whole Palace bristled with the whispers, from drawing-room to scullery and stable. The more charitable suggested that, at worst, she might have been secretly married, but the possibility of that as an excuse was dismissed as almost equally sinful. At that stage only the Queen and her mother and Lady Flora herself were ignorant of the tale, but it did not take long for two of Flora's fellow Ladies of the Bedchamber to decide that it was their bounden duty to pass on this tit-bit to the Queen. Barely twenty years old herself, Victoria consulted her Prime Minister, Lord Melbourne (as she constantly did when problems arose in the days before 'Dear Albert' was there to advise).

Lord Melbourne's response was to consult Sir James Clark, who is believed to have denied the scandal so vehemently that no further official steps were taken in the matter for the time being. Certainly Lady Flora was neither punished nor banished. But neither were any steps taken to nail the slander and save her from humiliation, or to silence the busybodies from further tattle. Perhaps the Queen found the whole situation an embarrassment and with her advisers thought the rumours would die away when they became patently untrue, and that it would be kindlier not to have them come unnecessarily to the ears of the sensitive victim.

But over the following few weeks the knowing matrons and

131

winking footmen observed with 'distressed' satisfaction that Lady Flora's waistline was visibly expanding, and new credence was given to the malicious gossip. Many claimed to find it disgraceful that a young woman of such very doubtful virtue was attending on the mother of the unmarried young Queen.

Sir James Clark now felt obliged to tell Lady Flora of the accusation concerning her condition, and that he would do his best to refute it. But nothing he could do eased his patient's obvious shock and anguish as she began to be aware of the scandal about her reverberating round the whole court circle and household.

Far too much attention, in Lord Melbourne's opinion, was now being paid to the matter, attention that would be better focussed on other affairs of the country and he thought there was a great deal too much energy expended in trying to detect a guilty demeanour in any of the gentlemen of the court. The Prime Minister had no wish to allow several more months to pass before the question of guilt or innocence was resolved. And so it was decided that Lady Flora should be re-examined by, not only Sir James Clark but another physician, Sir Charles Clarke who had been the Loudon family doctor since Lady Flora's birth. Then the truth could be told.

The two examined the stricken girl carefully again, and pronounced her quite innocent, but seriously ill with a growing abdominal cancer. The rumours died away, with shamefaced matrons and maidens insisting that they, at least, had never believed them from the start, but waiting suspiciously nevertheless to see what the end of the summer would bring.

Lady Flora sank lower. The shame, indignity and disgrace compounded most bitterly the tragedy of her terminal illness. Only six months after her first visit to Sir James Clark she died, as the old records put it, 'in great mental and bodily distress, of the abdominal swelling which had first given rise to all the speculation'.

There never was public acknowledgement of the wrong done to Lady Flora Hastings, although the young Queen privately expressed her own regrets. Flora's own brother and her mother made earnest protestations and when some time later a small volume of her poems was published, it is said that the general tone of these reflected to its readers a perceptively religious nature, which must have been tortured at the suggestions circulating about her during her illness, and the witholding of the ordinary sympathy which might otherwise have supported her last days.

The Inventor of Ochiltree

There have been other men, throughout the ages, besides Leonardo da Vinci and the brothers Wright, who have believed so truly in the power of men to fly, that they expended much energy and time trying to discover the secret.

Such a man was Willum Thomson, a weaver of a century and a half ago who lived in Ochiltree.

In his greenstick years he tried unassisted flight, his arms flailing, his legs taut and held tight together like a bird's tail, taking off from rocks above the Lugar water and from the trees providing wind-break to the Minister's glebe. But bruisings and grazings were all he had to show for that theory and, as he grew to manhood he began to study more intently the construction of bird anatomy and the aerodynamics of their wing work.

The truth dawned on him one morning when his attention wandered (as it did too often, and brought the wrath of his new wife down on his dreamy head) to the peasweeps on the moor outside his open door. He thumped his fist three times on his forehead and might have cried 'Eureka' had he been acquaint with the Greek. 'It was the feathers that swep' up the plovers from the field!' If he was to take two of his feathered weaver-fans and tie them one under each oxter, he was certain sure he could just flee away into the air from the lum of his cottage gable.

Now Willum would have liked fine to be of the stuff that puts dreams and theories to the test at once and come out of the ordeal covered modestly with glory. But he was not made like that and he rumbled the idea about in his head talking of it without cease until the men of Ochiltree were tired hearing of it. The women-folk had never listened anyway, for they said among themselves that he was dited and would do better to get his head down heartier to his loom.

But the boys of Ochiltree never tired of hearing of weaver Willum's notion and Willum never knew when curious spiering ended and wicked tormenting began.

One day in the spring of the year, the bolder spirits among the boys sat on his yard wall and got the inventor worked up to such a fierce pitch of enthusiastic certainty about his theory that at last he was persuaded to put flight to the test.

133

'I must wear my right claddin', mind.' Two of the lads marched with him into his indignant wife's kitchen to help him change and, in their hurry lest he renege from his decision, they buttoned him into his jacket down the back. But it was the feather fans that mattered, and buttons one way or the other would surely never hinder flight. Anyway, Willum himself did not notice.

They coaxed him up the thatch to his lum in full feather, then stood back and clapped and cheered their encouragement.

Then, trying hard not to misdoubt his own cleverness, he launched himself into space, into the blue April sky and flew, straight down into his household midden.

The boys fled round the gable corner and came back only when they heard a distinct groan.

'You're no' deid then, Willum?' they asked thankfully. The answer came in tones of impending death.

'No, but I cannae have long, I think, for my heid's twisted right roon on my neck.'

The Tailor's Apprentice

Time was in Ayrshire when tailors were itinerant craftsmen doing their round of farms to work, and going home only for every Sabbath. Instead of having busy farmworkers bring their woven cloths to tailors' workshops to be measured and fitted, tailors took their shears and threads with maybe a man and an apprentice, and had two or three days hospitality while they made up suits of homespun for all the menfolk of a steading.

Rab Hunter was such a tailor and Gabriel Walker his measurer and cutter. With them on a spring circuit the Year-of-the-Big-Snow near the turn of the 18th to the 19th century, they took young Willie Catrine to sweep up their clippings, write down their measures and keep his eyes peeled to learn his trade. Their first job that week was at Burnside Farm.

It was work fraught with indignities for the lad, for the two men took every opportunity of sending him on foolish errands, for single-bladed scissors or invisible chalk, and of playing pranks against him to excite the admiring giggles of any unwed serving-wenches or daughters of the house. But Willie Catrine was not so easily floored. He was a quick lad and already skeely with shears and needle, anxious to get on with this trade of his where, as well as earn an independent living, a man got wholesome farm vittles and a warm bed at nights. He had had a poor home with scant food, living with a drunken aunt and uncle and the taste he had had that first morning at Burnside Farm of good creamed porridge had so excited him that he was foolish enough to tell Rab and Gabriel that he 'couldnae wait for his supper of the same dish'.

When the boy was out with his sweepings at the midden, Rab told the hovering servant-lass that when she set out the cream porridge for him and Gabriel, just to give young Willie only mealie water, for the other was too rich for him and made him bokey.

Manfully and politely the apprentice supped his watery gruel, but there was a gleam in his observant eye when he detected a smirk on the cream frilled lips of his tormentors. Later when the men were out puffing their pipes at the yett, Willie won a coggie of his own creamy parritch from the servant girl, and a kiss forbye. And he bided his time.

Next day he was having a private crack with two of the stalwart
farm sons who were being fitted for their new Sabbath breeches and,
with a regretful shake of his red head, he told them quietly that the
master-tailor was a bawbee 'off the shilling' from time to time
nowadays and took fits of dangerous wildness, when he might grab
the shears and try to do an injury to any in the room. His fits were
brief but he had to be overpowered and laid firmly on his back on the
floor, for everyone's good when they did come on.

'How d'you ken when it's comin'?' asked one of the sons.

'That's easy done, for he thumps on the table with his hand a minute before he goes daft. He's about due another attack for he hasnae had one since last week there.'

Next day the kitchen was a-bustle with tailoring, washing and cooking, the two great sons were standing pinned and tacked in their breeches, their eyes gimlet-ready for trouble. Rab, the master tailor, was groping about across the work-table for the shears he could not immediately locate by eye, and to make them jingle he thumped the table smartly with his hand. In an instant the tailor-dummies leapt on him, pitched him to the sanded flagstone floor where they sat astride him with their hard-muscled hurdies and held his flailing fists with great broad hands that held ploughs and kept horses in order. The tailor kicked and spluttered and gave good evidence of being in a fit, but he was shirpit wee man and no match for brawny farmers.

Only when exhaustion made him lie like a raggy doll, did his warders let him up. He dusted himself down and the earnestness of young Willie's diligent attention to his sweepings caught his eye.

'Are you a' right?' asked one of the farm sons kindly. 'Fits like that must be a heavy burden for you, right enough.'

'Aye, aye,' said the tailor drily as he dusted himself down. 'But tell me, how did you ken that I was that way inclined?'

'It was a blessing your laddie told us or you might have done someone an injury.' The tailor turned a baleful eye on Willie.

'I see, I see ... and you, boy, when did you first discover my weakness?' he asked.

'Two-three minutes after you found out I couldnae stomach the cream parritch.' And Willie brushed the more busily at the cloth snippings on the flagstones.

Sketches of Genius

1

THE SECOND SIGHT

The woman shifted uneasily in her seat by the ingle aware that the time was come for the birth of her first child. The clay-bound cot her man had built to house their marriage, shuddered in the storm that shrieked outside across the countryside of Kyle, and neighbour women who might in better weather have known of her plight were sitting snug by their own hearthsides. And there was no kinswoman there either to see her through her delivery.

Another pain shot through her too soon after the last and her man, her tall stern man, gently touched her head in blessing.

'Be you easy Nannie I'll awa' to Ayr for a woman, a midwife woman you must have for this first.'

Agnes smiled a brave and fearful smile. 'Mind yoursel' in the storm William,' she whispered and then gathered herself together again in the next surge of pain. He eased himself into his coat and let himself ben the house to saddle his horse.

He rode through wild and windy darkness over ground that was not yet quite familiar to him, for he was not native to these parts. A less godly man might have cursed when his way was suddenly obstructed by a wide, bridgeless burn, high that night in spate. But William merely tightened his lips and made to wade through it with the horse, for there was no time to lose looking for a diversion. Then, as he dragged his boots through the tumbling water he saw, on the far bank, an old woman whimpering and frightened and wanting to cross, but afraid of the rushing stream.

William reached her, threw his reins over a tree stump and silently carried the woman back to the other side of the burn. She muttered her thanks and made to put a lucky hand on him, but he brushed it away as a superstitious gipsy nonsense and plunged hastily across the stream to leap on to his mare and make up for lost time by urging her the faster towards Ayr.

When William arrived home later with the midwife, he found the gipsy wayfarer-woman sitting at his own hearth, taking comfortable shelter from the storm, and keeping Agnes company during her

138

labour with tales of her wandering adventures and by foretelling great things for the coming bairn.

There was a shout from Agnes and then a moan of relief and triumph as her son was born. The midwife, a kindly white-mutched woman, wrapped him in the rough warm shawl his mother had made ready and handed him to the gipsy while she turned her skills and attention back to the weary Agnes. The old wife heeshie-bawed the baby and examined his tiny palm.

'He'll be a rare one this, a braw clever laddie to make his mother proud. See this lines too ... he'll maybe no' have greatly siller in his pooch, but we'll a' mind this night of his coming.'

William did not care to hear in his house such sinful tampering with a future which his Calvanist God would surely reveal in his own good time, but maybe he remembered it in later years with the uneasy suspicion that the gipsy-woman might just have had a glimmering of the second sight.

It is not claimed by devotees of Robin Burns or by collectors of lore and fable about him, that even his genius was up to remembering the night of his birth and the old woman sitting there prophesying. But he did certainly later picture the scene in that storm-bound clay cottage ...

> The gossip keekit[1] in his loof[2]
> Quoth she who lives will see the proof
> This waly[3] boy will be nae coof[4]
> I think we'll ca' him Robin
> He'll hae misfortunes great and sma'
> But aye a heart abune[5] them a';
> He'll be a credit to us a',
> We'll a' be proud o' Robin.

---

[1]looked   [2]palm   [3]clever   [4]fool   [5]above

139

TAM

William Burnes was first a small market gardener and then the peasant farmer of only a few acres, and he must have thought it more than probable that his sons would follow in his measured footsteps behind the plough. But he was nevertheless firm in his determination to enrich their minds if not their 'pooches', by dinning into them the value of education and making it possible for them to have as much of it as he could manage to give them. Accordingly they became steeped in history, Latin, mythology, geography and literature and in 1775 when Robin was sixteen he was sent to learn 'mensuration' or basic surveying in the village of Kirkoswald.

The young man's own home was that of 'The Cotter's Saturday Night,' godly, regular, moral, conscientious and serious, and if the honest William had foreseen the company awaiting his eldest son at Kirkoswald he might have left the subject of measuring out of his boy's curriculum. For Robin was not long settled in the village when he fell in with a breed of men, quite new and exciting to him, of smuggler-farmers and craftsmen, who led a swaggering and lusty life, who boldly evaded the Carrick excisemen and celebrated their tax-free spoils by carousing together in the local taverns. To be sure Burns did not join them in their exploits but he lurked on the fringes of their society, admiring from a distance and glorying in the over-hearing and reclashing of their wild and rollicking infamy. The two outstanding men in these colourful circles were Douglas Graham of Shanter Farm and John Davidson the Kirkoswald soutar, along with their two closest disciples, the miller and the blacksmith.

At sixteen, Robin found the tales he heard of Mistress Douglas Graham of Shanter (Nellie McTaggart that was) distasteful and diminishing to the bigness of her wild man. For it was said that he cringed when she scolded him if he was late home from Ayr market after a drouthy evening over the whisky. She was fiercely superstitious always, that he had been waylaid by Satan's warlocks. Robin preferred to forget these tales and the proof he had had of them himself one day during that stay at Kirkoswald, which lay only a few miles from the sea.

He and two friends had been out fishing and a great storm had arisen while they were some distance from shore. It frightened them half to death for an hour or more, but they had made safe to land not far from Shanter Farm. The storm was at its height and with rain deluging on them they had thought to take shelter at Douglas Graham's farmhouse. There the good Nellie McTaggart, Mistress Graham, had entertained them to a warming stoup and a platter of bread and cheese and also to her loud complaints that her gudeman was never back yet from Ayr market. He was like-enough, she told them, toping away with soutar, smith and miller and laying himself wide-open to evil powers waiting to do him mortal harm. When Graham did come in he had tried to divert her scolding by telling how his good grey mare, tethered outside the inn at Ayr, had had the hairs plucked wantonly from her tail by local boys for fishing lines, that it was now straggling and thin and that he had wasted good time he would rather have spent with his own wee wife, trying to find the culprits. But for all his invention the brave Douglas had been bettered by Mistress Nellie and Burns would have liked fine to forget the shrewish belittling of his idol he witnessed that day.

But he did not forget it and as he grew older the humour of the whole situation began to tickle his maturing sense of humour. For fourteen years it lay germinating in his shaggy, black poetic head along with another half-buried memory from his childhood of an old witch-story concerning Alloway Kirk. The tale told of a farmer going home from market half-drunk and seeing a fearsome dance of witches taking place in the church. Then, half his lifetime after the stay in Kirkoswald, the seeds grew into shoots and Robin tangled them together; the staying too late at the inn, the plucking of the mare's tail, Nellie McTaggart's fears for her man, the bewitching of the farmer at Alloway. And out of them all, between breakfast and dinner in one day of 1790 the poet wove the tale of 'Tam o' Shanter' one of his most quoted and enduring works.

Douglas Graham of Shanter became Tam, and his friend David-son Soutar Johnnie, Nellie McTaggart playing the wife at home waiting, the

> ... sulky sullen dame,
> Gathering her brows like gathering storm,
> Nursing her wrath to keep it warm.

The old grey horse that Burns recalled from past days at Shanter Farm became Tam's mare Meg, and even the hat that Graham wore gave the name of Tam o' Shanter ever after to tooried bonnets all over the world.

So, Burns' story runs, Tam o' Shanter sat enjoying himself in the ale-house after market, with Soutar Johnnie.

>   ... boozin'[1] at the nappy[2]
>   And gettin' fu' and unco[3] happy ...
>   But pleasures are like poppies spread
>   You seize the flower, its bloom is shed;
>   Or, like the snow falls in the river,
>   A moment white — then melts for ever.

And so he must for home, through a dark winter's night wild with storm. In sober moments Tam would have given Alloway Kirk a wide skirt, but he was bold from the nappy and allowed his good grey mare to carry him to the windows of the Kirk, for some strange unchancy reason brightly lit that night. Through the window he saw a fearsome sight with Auld Nick himself presiding over it.

>   Warlocks and witches in a dance:
>   No cotillion new frae France,
>   But hornpipes, jigs, strathspeys and reels
>   Put life and mettle in their heels.

Tam shouted in gleeful appreciation of the wild cantrips of the bogles, whereupon the whole legion of them swarmed after him,

>   As bees bizz out wi' angry fyke[4]
>   When plundering herds assail their byke;

While Meg the mare, bolted toward the old Brig o' Doon. Terrified of being captured for Hell, Tam urged on the horse,

>   Now do thy speedy utmost Meg,
>   And win the keystone of the brig;
>   There at them, thy tail may toss
>   A running stream they dare not cross!

Meg did win the keystone of the bridge but she sacrificed her tail when the leading witch,

>   ... caught her by the rump
>   And left poor Maggie scarce a stump.

Burns ends his tale with a solemn warning of the price to be paid by such as Tam o' Shanter, who stay too late at inns on market days.

---

[1]drinking [2]ale [3]more than [4]bustle

3

THE GEM

'Tam' took fourteen years to flower in Robert Burns' mind but other short verses were almost instant on the episodes that inspired them.

Towards the end of his life the poet, visiting a friend, met two ladies, the one portly, tall and less than lovely, the other petite and pretty — a second guest commented to the poet that it was strange God had made one so dainty and the other so massive. Burns replied at once in verse.

> Ask why God made the gem so small
> And why so huge the granite
> Because God meant mankind should set
> The higher value on it.

4

LOVING AND LOSING

Defying his father's strict will, Robin had decided it was time for him to brush up the image he had of himself as country clod-hopper by attending the dancing at Ronald's jig-room in Mauchline.

Poverty and sour soil had dogged the Burns menfolk and in Robin's youth they had moved anxiously from farm to farm in Ayrshire seeking meagre prosperity. Now for the present they were settled at Mossgiel Farm near Mauchline. And Robin was widening the circle of his friends.

It was a spring evening when he first went to the dancing-room and there were few female hearts that did not flutter at the sight of him. He was twenty-six years old now, a well set-up lad, broad-shouldered and dark-eyed with curling dark hair, and the girls thought he must have spent near his life's earnings on his shiny buckled shoon and blue-cloth coat with the white linen cravat at his throat.

The natural rhythm in him that romped through his poems pulsed also in his feet, and the brain that had studied 'Physico-Astro Theology' and 'Harvey's Meditations' in childhood soon mastered the intricacies of strathspeys and reels. He whirled admiring lasses until they were dizzy, the fiddle-bow flew, feet thudded, hands clapped and soon the evening was gone.

The first few revellers making for home left the hall door open and from outside where he had been patiently waiting, a collie dog streaked across the floor to claim his master. Robin bent down and slapped the animal playfully.

'Luath, Luath, you'll be an end of me. If I could but find a lass as faithful!'

There was a lass, just as faithful, there among the dancers that night. Burns had noticed Jean Armour in the room then, and over the summer he met her on his evening danders about Mauchline, and on tub-days when she was trampling her whites on the village wash green. They smiled, they talked, they soon fell in love and by the back-end of the year had exchanged unkirked but written marriage vows.

Both regarded them as binding and were ready to settle to married life, but Jean's father, James Armour, had no time for Rab Burns of the poor Mossgiel Farm and of the even poorer reputation with the lasses. He repudiated the poet utterly as his daughter's husband and destroyed their marriage paper.

Robin took his smouldering pride away and found solace in a serious and passionate romance with a dairymaid at a local farm, his Highland Mary, whom some have called bewitching and others inexplicably plain. They exchanged Bibles over a running stream, the symbol of earnest intent ...

> She has my heart she has my hand,
> My secret troth and honour's band!
> Till mortal stroke shall lay me low,
> I'm thine, my Highland Mary — O.

Beset now by financial problems, still hurt and angry over Jean Armour, but feeling he might make a happy marriage with Mary Campbell if they were far away, Burns decided to emigrate with her to Jamaica. Their arrangements were made by early that summer and he awaited only word of a suitable passage and news of the publication of his first collection of poems. Mary meanwhile went to visit her parents.

And then his plans changed dramatically when his Kilmarnock published poems appeared on July 31st 1786.

They were highly praised by a discerning Edinburgh poet and critic, the Reverend Dr. Blacklock, and they brought him a modest financial return. In these two encouraging facts he glimpsed a change of fortune and decided that his future lay in Scotland after all.

By now Mary Campbell had been taken ill and had died, lonely for

Robin, in a small apartment in Greenock while waiting for her promised husband who never came ...

Stricken with remorse for his neglect, Burns wrote his 'Highland Mary'.

> Wi' many a vow and locked embrace
> Our parting was fu' tender;
> And pledging oft to meet again,
> We tore ourselves asunder.
> But oh! fell death's untimely frost
> That nip't my flower sae early!
> Now green's the sod, and cauld's the clay
> That wraps my Highland Mary!

And then Robin cheered up enough to enjoy his literary success and enjoyed a light-hearted flirtation with Agnes McLehose in Edinburgh which gave rise to a lyrical correspondence conducted above the noms de plume of 'Sylvander' and 'Clarinda'.

But then he turned his attention back to the abiding love of his life Jean Armour. He went home to Mauchline to claim her as his wife, this time with the first flush of fame on him, this time accepted by her father.

> Of a' the airts[1] the wind can blaw
> I dearly like the west,
> For there the bonnie lassie lives,
> The lassie I lo'e best.
> I see her in the dewy flowers —
> I see her sweet and fair
> I hear her in the tunefu' birds
> I hear her charm the air.
> There's not a bonnie flower that springs
> By fountain, shaw, or green,
> There's no' a bonnie bird that sings,
> But minds me o' my Jean.

Robin settled happily to family life at Ellisland Farm, still writing his poetry and songs, and still indulging in a variety of philanderings which the generous Jean forgave. And she had not only the living loves of her man to contend with. On the third anniversary of the day when Burns had heard of Mary Campbell's death in Greenock, Jean tells us that he was slightly fevered with a cold but worked cheerfully at the harvest until dusk when he came into the house restless and not able to settle at the ingle. He grew quiet, even

---

[1] directions

melancholy, and wandered alone into a chilly September evening in the yard. Jean remembered later that she called him once or twice fearing the cold for the weakness he had in his chest, but he seemed not to hear. Later she went out looking for him with a lantern, and found him at last, near midnight, lying below a haystack his great dark eyes glowing in the moonlight. This time he did come in but sat down at once and wrote, as easily as if it had been a poem he had been reciting since childhood, 'To Mary in Heaven'.

> That sacred hour can I forget,
> Can I forget the hallowed grove,
> Where by the winding Ayr we met,
> To live our day of parting love?
> Eternity will not efface
> Those records dear of transports past;
> Thy image at our last embrace;
> Ah! little thought we 'twas our last!

He laid down his repentant quill and the great-hearted Jean gave him a warm bedtime sup to break his fever.

5

FROM A' THE AIRTS

Robin Burns lay struggling for breath his limbs a dead weight and, in contrast, his fevered head seeming to swim further and further away from him so that every now and then he had to catch it back and try to order its fluttering escaping thoughts.

From time to time when he had them there safe with him he could concentrate on the great shadow of Jean cast by the firelight on the wall, cumbersome with the child she would bear with the week. She was weary with nursing him and tending the rest of their bairns, and moved slowly. God forgive him! He had misused Jean; faithful to her in mind and heart but ah! fell wayward with his body. She struggled now over the ingle and weakly he called the girl from the other room to come and help his wife.

She came running across the bare floor and took the scuttle from Mistress Burns with a scolding voice no sharper than a cushi-doo's. Robin watched the lissom figure of young Jessy Lewars and knew fine that if he had not been a dying man and she had been willing, he would have betrayed Jean, dear Jean, yet again.

Instead he whispered for them to bring him his writing-box. They found two poems on his bed when they came on him asleep later; the

146

first was 'O wert Thou in the Cauld Blast,' and the more lilting final poem of his life,

> Here's a health to ane I lo'e dear!
> Here's a health to ane I lo'e dear!
> Thou art sweet as the smile when fond lovers meet
> And soft as their parting tear, Jessy —
> And soft as their parting tear.

In the midsummer of 1796, in poverty and two days before the birth of his son Maxwell, Robert Burns died of chronic heart disease. In his latter years he had thought himself half-forgotten. But if he could have been a ghost in Dumfries on the day of his funeral he would have been astonished, moved perhaps to compose some wry little ditty on life's irony, when he saw the many thousands of people of all classes and from all accessible parts of Scotland who followed his coffin through the streets to see him laid to rest in the town kirkyard.

One can scarcely omit from a book of Ayrshire lore a few of the traditions surrounding some of the works of Robert Burns. Undoubtedly Scotland's most famous son, he was the man who knew, better than almost any other, her folk tales and ancient legends. Indeed he was himself so huge a part of Ayrshire and Scottish mythology that he cries out for inclusion in this volume.

People world-wide have ever been curious about the inspiration which drew such a stream of poetry and song from a largely self-educated peasant farmer whose everyday life was a constant struggle against poverty, ill-health and the arid soil of poor farms, and who died when he was thirty-seven. So curious have they been that in every generation since his death they have dug deep, not only into his work, but into his life for answers to their questions.

These sketches include quotations which are certainly not of his finest work, but have been selected as some of those round which tradition has grown into part of the folkweave which haps his memory, and also because of their aptness for this book. There is nothing here of the enduring literature he made of his outcry against cant and hypocrisy and the plight of the common man of his own time. That work came from his core and not from casual incidents or the suggestions of others.

The Fisher of Carrick

One fine summer evening a Carrick fisher sat, hard by the Castle of Turnberry, in a tiny rocky cove concealed from prying eyes. The sun was setting behind the Arran hills with their deep scars and rugged peaks. Tradition names him only as William of the Maidens, the village lying low across the shore-land. He was a sea-going fisher-lad used to the storms and lashing rains of the Firth of Clyde and the Atlantic beyond, used too to the toils of hauling nets and struggling with blatting sails. Ashore, his fellow fishermen roistered in the ale-houses or tramped the hills. But William was never happy inland and, when not sailing the sea, liked nothing better than to sit on the rocks beside it on fair evenings and fish the quiet way with rod and line.

This was just such a time and the rocks where he sat formed a small promontory reaching out some thirty yards into the bay so that there was depth enough to try for the plump little fish that swam in the Turnberry waters. Ahead of him, some twenty ells apart like giant stepping-stones sat the three rocks where credulous Maidens folk said that the Sea People sat in the sun.

William was as simple as the lave of the village shore-folk but there was a queer nub of thrawness in him that had never taken to the tales of bogles and kelpie creatures in the hinterland, or to stories of the mer-people ... tales that were gospel to most Carrick folk from laird to cot-lad, as they were to town and country people the length and breadth of Scotland. William, however, scorned what he did not know and he had never yet met land-bogle or sea-witch.

It was therefore with some puzzlement that three times that evening when bites trembled along his line and he played-in three silver fish and laid them to thrash themselves still on the rock, he heard, coming quite distinctly from them in three voices varying upwards in pitch, earnest pleas to be thrown back into their home waters. It was unnerving; but speaking fish were one thing, fairies of the sea-depths another, and yet a third (and quite the most appealing) was a good grilling of caller fish for his supper, so he slithered them into his creel and paid no heed to their entreaties. They arc'd, gasped out their plea once or twice more and then lay quiet in the basket.

His fish were rare and fresh, and sat comfortable inside him that evening along with a jug of ale. He slept dreamlessly all that night and, next day being the Sabbath, dutifully made his two kirk observances. But mindful of the fine supper the night before, he was tempted of Satan to break the Lord's Day and he slipped off quietly, with rod and line hid under his shirt and down his breeches, to his hidden little bay.

But the Turnberry fish were not biting that night and the lad sat patiently without feeling the slightest twitch to his line. The waves shrugged and lapped against the promontory and splashed against the rocks in the bay; and gradually William became aware of a strange, weird kind of moaning. He listened. It was a singing sound, haunting and enticing ... a woman's singing, or a young boy's maybe. It seemed to come from the first of the stepping rocks, but William could see no one there. The tones of the song were clearer now and the fisherlad could not resist following them. The singer must be on that near rock. He laid his rod where he had been sitting and waded out to the rock, the voice, piercing and sweet, drawing him on. But the rock was empty of any singer and so were the shrugging waters round it. Still it sang, farther off then, surely from the second rock. The sea was round his waist but the glammer was cast on him and he was solemn certain that he would find some exquisite creature on the second rock. He drew near the place, but the voice faded again farther yet into the distance. The second rock was empty and he searched the waters round it in vain. Now the distant voice was filled with longing, now it was sobbing as if for lost souls. Breast deep in the water William was lured on, wading manfully towards the third rock. The sun had sunk behind the hills of Arran and a wind was whipping up cream-crested waves as darkness gathered. Experienced as he was in the cruel ways of the sea in storm, the same sea he loved in summer calm, the down-to-earth William would have turned and made back for the shore when such a squall arose. But this was another William, spellbound and will-less, drawn on by the invisible singer, who seemed as far off now as Ailsa Craig, and he was buffeted helpless by the pitching sea, stung sorely by its spray.

They say (though how they *know* is as much a mystery as the tale) that the last words William of The Maidens heard before the dark seas closed over his head were a lamentation by a mer-witch for three lost children, lost from the shallow fishing waters of the firth. Who can tell for truth? Nevertheless the tale became part of the lore of the Carrick shorelands and was told, for generations, as a warning to the children of the fisher-folk.

The Burglar of the Brandy-Hole

It was a queer thing that John McAdam, who was otherwise a douce Dundonald householder and firm in his allegiance to minister and kirk, should be sitting, nonetheless, considering a case of brandy and a kist of tea which he had surreptitiously removed two days before from a smuggle-hole at Harpercroft farm. And on a Sabbath evening at that!

This was his first fall into the sin of stealing from the smugglings. His conscience was by now rankling sorely from the double sin and he was much put-about in his mind what best to do with the ill-gotten takings now. In a rush of righteousness to the head after the morning's preaching, he had told himself that he was just keeping it for a prank and really meant to give it back. The truth was that, too late, he was realising that he would soon be discovered if he tried to sell it. He was not a great man for the bottle himself (although he enjoyed an occasional hazy evening) and there was enough tea in the chest for more years than he was like to live. It was the money, that he had thought vaguely might be somewhere in it, that had tempted him to the theft in the first place.

How to give it back safe and sound and yet line his pocket a wee bit forbye? That was the nub of what John McAdam chewed over that Sabbath night. Then a slow smile spread over his lean face and he blew out the candle and went to sleep.

Next day after work he put himself alongside the Harpercroft farmer, the man who had concealed the smuggled cargo from which John had helped himself, and who had been complaining bitterly (under his breath for fear of the gaugers) that some sinner-rat had nibbled his store.

'I'm for Kilmarnock the night,' began John. 'If you like I could have a word to a spaewife I'm acquaint with as to the whereabouts of your stuff *and* the thief. It'll cost you a guinea mind, for her fee.'

A guinea was a heavy sum, but a cask of brandy and a kist of tea were more, and the coin was handed over.

John McAdam went to Kilmarnock and had a fine spree with the guinea and if he looked a bit the worse for wear when he came back the good folk of Dundonald put it down to the dreadful fright he told them he had had there. It was a different spaewife this time, he said.

'I was put into a dark room,' he related to old Harpercroft first, 'and the smell of brimstone was overpowerful, and the moaning and screeching was no' earthly. There was a fizzing and scooshing of blue light and in a muckle great mirror I saw Harpercroft farm, clear as clear, as if I was standing looking at it, and the hills behind it. Then it went clean out o' sight and the old wife wanted another guinea off me, before she would show me whereaboots to go and find your lost stuff. I paid her, Master Harpercroft sir, for I knew I would have it back from you when I came home.' The farmer nodded and fished it from his pocket. 'Then there was that ungodly blue light again and the noise that made my very hair stand on end and this time I saw, just as clear, the case of whisky and the box of tea, sitting there on Warliehill bush. Then I fainted and dreamed a terrible dream of monsters and slime pits and slavering beasts. Three times I had that, before the spaewoman bid me go and find the whin bush.' John McAdam looked earnestly at the loser of the smugglings. 'You can go and see her yourself if you've a mind, Harpercroft.'

But neither Harpercroft, nor any of the knot of hangers-on now gathered, had any notion to see the spaewife. They went instead to the whin bush and found the tea and brandy there, just as the second-sighted old woman had said they would be.

And that was the tale of how John McAdam salved his conscience by restoring the goods to their unrightful owner and yet had a guinea's worth of cantrips in Kilmarnock and another guinea to hand over to his gudewife, as an honourable and upright citizen should always do with an unexpected bonus.

Nor was that the last time John McAdam bravely bearded that awful den in Kilmarnock, to help a robbed smuggler recover goods stolen from his hidey-hole (for most of the menfolk in these parts had a regular share in the trade). There were more ways, thought John, of dabbling in the excise-running, than the risky business of facing armed gaugers at the arriving-place of a contraband cargo in Troon or wherever.

The incoming of illicit luxuries on the rugged Scottish coast made an almost laughable impact on peasant life there, adding to porridge-kail, salt-herring and homespun lives tea, spirits, silks and fine French wines. Douce farmers grew lazy over their milking and their wives made porridge with brandy instead of cream. It is even said that on one occasion, it being too much trouble to bring in water from the well to drink in their brandy, they adjourned to the well with a keg, tipped-in its contents and ladled out the mixture to drink until it was dilute enough to sober up the topers again.

151

The Berwick Ambush

Sir John Cochrane of Ochiltree lay in despair in the Tolbooth of Edinburgh. He was awaiting sentence of death for his part in the Rye House plot to put the Duke of Monmouth (natural son of Charles II) on the throne in place of his legitimately born uncle James II. Sir John had been concerned in that rising under the leadership of the Earl of Argyll. Now Argyll was about to be executed, Monmouth himself was already dead, and so there was little likelihood that John Cochrane would be spared.

He had certainly not been entirely a man of honour during his devious public life, in which plotting against the king had been only one of his intrigues. But he had ever been a fond husband and father, and his family was greatly distressed at the prospect of his death. His friends knew that only an appeal to James II of some tempting kind, would win his freedom and pardon. James could be a vindictive man to any who threatened his throne, but he was also an avaricious man and might just fall to the offer of gold or kind if he could be faced with rich enough temptation.

The Heart of Midlothian, the dreary dungeon where the Ayrshire laird was lodged, was a place of tragic memory, from which many before him through the ages had gone to the block; as most were certain Cochrane would do too whenever the order came north from London. He felt sure himself when his wife and family came up from Ochiltree to see him, that they were saying good-bye to him for ever. And indeed they had come to Edinburgh intending to stay until the execution had been ordered and carried out.

One of the Cochrane family come to Edinburgh to lament Sir John's fate was his daughter Grisell. She was strong and brave, independent and intelligent and, although she shared their grief, she did not share their despair. She was impatient for her father's friends to act on his behalf and she puzzled her own fertile brain for a plan to save him outright from his fate or even to delay his execution long enough for these friends to find a plan to persuade the king. She looked at the problem this way and that ... if she could only gain a little time. She absorbed every piece of information she could ferret out about the procedures and the routines followed between the passing of the sentence and its being carried out, and she sifted through it all for a plan.

She consulted a time or two with young lawyer Ker of Moriston in Berwickshire, who told her that within a few days the Privy Council would be sending a warrant to Edinburgh for the execution to go ahead and that no death penalty could be carried out without that warrant. While he was advising Grisell the young man became more and more stricken with the charms which were apparent in spite of her distress over her father's predicament. Had he known what use she intended to make of the information he had already given her, he would no doubt have bitten out his tongue.

Grisell went home thoughtfully from her last meeting with Lawyer Ker. If she could intercept the warrant and stop the execution, that would give her father's friends valuable time. She built up her plot, detail by intrepid detail, told no one and said to her father only that she could not visit him for a few days. But Sir John knew his daughter and was afraid that she had some foolhardy plan in mind. He warned her to take no risks for him.

'I am an Ochiltree Cochrane,' was all she said and lightly kissed him good-bye.

Early next morning, before Edinburgh was about its business, Grisell dressed herself as a servant lass, save for the brace of pistols she put in her kirtle. She took a horse from her host's stable, led it out and sprang up as lightly as if she was about to take a canter about the hills of Kyle. A sleepy watchman admired her saddle seat and twenty minutes later the city-gate keeper, who opened up for her, wondered vaguely what took a serving-wench out beyond the town so early in the morning.

Once in the open country she gave the horse his head to get the feel of the day. Then she settled into a steady plod for the long ride that lay ahead to Berwick, the grey city of the Borders. She passed a night in a hostelry by the wayside and next day rode on through Berwick to a house she knew of four miles beyond the border with England. Here her own old nurse lived now in retirement and when she finally recognised her young lady, tousled and travel-stained, she reluctantly agreed to help her in her task. The woman trembled at the girl's recklessness, at her determination to intercept the courier bound for Edinburgh from London, and seize his mailbags. The nurse, clucking her disapproval all the while, lent her a suit of clothing belonging to her son, a slim built youth not much taller than the lissom Grisell.

Mail was brought from London, in the late days of the 17th

153

century, by relays of heavily armed post-boys instructed, if need
arose, to discharge their pistols at highwaymen or footpads. Anyone
taken in the obstruction of mails faced probable execution and this
Grisell Cochrane, like everyone else, knew full well.

The post-boy for this lap of the journey was due in the nearby
small town of Belford at 6 o'clock in the morning. When the girl
reached Belford change-house he had already arrived and was
stretched out fast asleep on a wooden settle by the fire, the mailbags
firmly under his head, his pistols at his hand. He was a rugged,
brawny looking fellow and she could see with a sinking heart that it
was useless to tackle him there. She sat down, called the old dame of
the hostelry and offered her the price of a glass of fine wine for only a
drink of water, fresh-drawn from the well. It was a fair offer, else the
woman would have grumbled at having to go out into her yard, and

154

while she was gone Grisell had time to withdraw the charges from the loose-lying guns and have them back at the man's hand, harmless, before her drink of water arrived.

'He's in a fair sleep, the post-boy,' she said pleasantly to the woman. 'Does he always sleep so sound?'

'He's sound enough the now, but he'll be up and gone before an hour's by.'

Grisell left shortly after, and rode off first to the south to avoid suspicion, then she swept round and rode back again in the opposite direction where in a grove of trees she changed her clothes. She rode on then and waited for her quarry at a cross-track some miles to the north. The post-boy duly left the Change-house and made fast northward too, where he soon came on a solitary horseman quietly jogging ahead of him. When he made up on the rider he was greeted by an effeminate youth who seemed pleased to have his company for a mile or two, since he pricked his horse to match the post-boy's speed. When they were narrowly enclosed in a track running through a stretch of woodland Grisell reined in a little clumsily against the post-horse and, to the mailman's consternation demanded his post-bags. He thought the stripling was jesting and laughed but the youth drew his pistols and told him he was only one of a large party hidden in the woods. Seeing that the 'boy' was serious he drew his own pistols and told the young highwayman that he would not hesitate to shoot if hands were laid on the bags.

'The bags an you please, Master post-boy,' insisted Grisell.

The mailman drew and fired his first impotent pistol and hesitated in only the briefest surprise before trying the second. He saw that they had been interfered with and threw them aside. Then he sprang from his saddle to unhorse her. But long years of childhood and youth galloping over the moors round Ochiltree and Cumnock had made her quick and expert in the saddle . . . too quick certainly for the post-boy. She seized the bridle of the mail-horse, with the bags hanging unguarded now across its back, and she cantered away with the animal alongside her own and left the furious post-boy sitting on the ground scratching his head.

He was afraid now of the accomplices from the wood and ran back to Belford to report his loss and tell of the attack of a huge and desperate highwayman. Meantime in the wood Grisell examined the bag and there she came on a padlocked inner pouch. She slit it open with a small knife-blade and out fell official-seeming documents in a

155

blue envelope bearing the government seal. Among them was one addressed to the Council in Edinburgh ... surely the paper she had risked so much to find. She opened the seal and read the instruction there that her father's execution was dated for the next week. Grisell trembled as she thought of the patient prisoner in the Tolbooth. She stood there among the trees and tore the missive into small pieces which she hid among her clothes, then she remounted her own horse and left the other quietly cropping at the grass.

She cantered towards Edinburgh all through the night, twice resting the horse by the wayside for short periods, and reached her host's home at dawn. Her mother was thankful to see her alive, for she had deep and terrifying suspicions that Grisell had put herself at some grave risk and that she herself might lose, not only husband, but beloved daughter as well.

The girl told her story in confidence to Lady Cochrane, and three or four gentlemen. They, awed by her courage, were more anxious than ever not to waste Grisell's escapade by letting her father die if they could possibly avert it. From other men of wealth they wheedled and cajoled enough yellow gold to tempt pardon from the king who was so partial to it. Armed with this money the Scottish lairds travelled to London to see James II.

Three weeks passed, giving the precious delay won by Grisell, before the lairds came back from London with the news that £5,000 in gold coin had been too much for the king to refuse. With them they brought back the royal pardon it had purchased for Sir John Cochrane. He was to be released from the Tolbooth and have restored to him his estates and privileges and the rights of eventual succession to the Earldom of Dundonald.

The mysterious affair of the Berwick robbery passed out of public mind, never solved in James II's time. For her own safety, not a soul spoke of Grisell's adventure until more than three years had passed. By then James Stuart had been deposed and exiled. There was a new regime under the House of Orange and no more need for silence on the matter. And then the Lowlands rang with her praise. In those years Lawyer Ker had furthered his acquaintance with the girl who had so attracted him, even as she was picking his Berwickshire brains, and it was a proud man who eventually carried the Highwayman of Belford over his threshold as Mistress Ker of Moriston, and out of the annals of Ayrshire.

156

Tammas Peacock Buys a Farm

Tammas Peacock was a travelling packman. He was garrulous and absorbent which made him a fund of gossip and tittle-tattle and a popular visitor when he did his monthly round in town and country. He liked his work well-enough in spring and summer when his feet were dry-shod and he could see the blackthorn blossom and the green flush rising over the hedgerows. But come the snell days with rime and Old Man's Beard at the roadside he thought many a time what a fine thing it would be to be a farmer.

In one of his Kyle ale-house haunts on an October night, as the first breath of winter wind lifted the floor-straw, he sat with one or two old acquaintances and another old fellow he had never met before. He sat comfortably in the blue coat with its gold buttons he had bought, cast-off, from an Edinburgh luckenbooth, and well-aled and mellow sighed so deeply that the unkent farmer asked what ailed him.

'Ah!' said Tammas, 'if I could just find a wee bit farm and stock it at a reasonable cost, I've a mind to settle down to the land and the animals. It's ower hard peddlin' trinkets up and doon the valleys.'

'So you're looking to the easy life of a farmin' man?' asked the old man.

'That's it,' agreed Tammas.

There was an Ayrshire twinkle in the eye of the ancient farmer.

'I've maybe a proposition for you then, young man.' He said he was going off to Ameriky to live with a married daughter and, for all the years he had left, had little need of getting a great price for his small bit-place.

'Since you're a well set-up young man wi' an honest face, I would make you an offer of my place at Gorsehill for a small price.' Tammas laid down his mug and wiped his mouth on the blue sleeve with its gold buttons.

'What's a small price?'

'Weel, would you give me maybe ...' The old man hesitated ... 'maybe a shilling a head for each of my beasts?' If so, he said he would throw in his new yett and the furbishing of his cottage for nothing.

Tammas could scarcely credit his luck, but he must be wily and not let the old man see his surprise.

157

'We could have it signed and sealed by Master Wilson, the lawyer there,' continued the farmer jerking his head towards a man in the corner. 'Would you undertake that, Master Wilson, sir?'

Master Wilson at the ingle clenched long serious jaws on his pipe. 'Indeed aye.'

Tammas was afraid that the old man would take back his generous offer and was greedy to get the papers signed. So the landlord produced writing materials, the simple clauses were written out and the lawyer witnessed the signature of the old emigrant and the mark of the fortunate Tammas Peacock, pedlar.

Next day Tammas presented himself at the well-tended and furnished cottage ready to go round and inspect his new-bought acres and stock at Gorsehill. They totted up ten cows and as many calves, a flock of thirty well-rounded sheep, two dozen fine-feathered laying fowl, eight pigs plump as peaches, a working dog, two sleek hunting cats and a sturdy pony. Tammas was not knacky with the lettering but he had eighty-six shillings summed up mentally long before the farmer mentioned the same figure.

'Weel then, that seems to be some eighty-sax shilling,' said the old man. 'Am I richt?'

'Exactly so, y'are,' agreed the pedlar hastily, scarcely able to conceal his astonished delight at this turn in his fortunes.

'Och there, and I near didnae mind. Come you to the yard at the back,' ordered the old man, and Tammas thought to see maybe a handsome black cockerel or some such treasure that the farmer had forgotten to count in. He followed the man round past the water-butt and into the back yard.

'There y'are now, that's what I very near forgot,' and he waved his hand at a row of twenty-seven hives lined up against the wall, with crawling bees massing black and gold around the entrances.

'Say three hunner bees to a hive ... at a shilling the heid ... that's ...,' the farmer scratched his head and began to work it out.

But Tammas had gone white at the thought of the papers he had been so hasty to put his mark to. Was he really to be wrong with the law for not being able to honour his deed?

'I think ...' he stammered hopefully, 'I'll maybe no' turn farmer after a'.'

'But the dockyments ...' protested the poker-faced farmer, whose only daughter lived, not in America, but a mile along the riverside at Crookedholm.

FIONA McFARLANE

'Would a five pound note do you and Master Wilson for your trouble?' quavered the fearful Tammas.

'Would it, Master Wilson?' asked the farmer, turning to the lawyer.

'Weel, it's no' very legal-like ... but maybe it would,' said the witness with never the glimmer of a smile.

Tammas Peacock handed it over and hurried back to his lodgings, seized his pedlar-tray and fled with it into Cuninghame.

He was not seen in these parts again till another year had come and gone. He met up in the inn with the farmer who bought him a dram for old time's sake and next day gave him twenty small gallipots of honey to sell from the pack-tray with his other gew-gaws. And every year until the old prankster really did emigrate to his lass at Crookedholm, Tammas Peacock was sure of a welcome and of his pots of honey when he passed the little farm at Gorsehill.

This story was told to the author by a lady from Darvel who said she had known it since childhood as local lore. One somewhat similar does appear, however, in *The Ayrshire Magazine* of 1816, where it is told of a Yorkshire pedlar.

The 'Flitting' of the Sow

Long long ago, some seven hundred years now, even before the Kennedy's began to feud among themselves, there was a long lasting and fierce vendetta between the Craufurds of Kyle and the Kennedys of Carrick. They provoked and taunted each other into skirmishes where sometimes one and sometimes the other would win the day and, careless of blood spilt, would go home to growl or boast at the result of the day's confrontation. Sometimes there was a reiving of the enemy's sheep or cattle or a firing of his keep. But the tale most often told to wide-eyed bairns in after-generations was that of the 'flitting' of the sow from the land of the Craufurds.

The territories of Craufurd and Kennedy faced each other across the River Doon and much of the feud involved spirited raids into each other's lands. The Chief of the Craufurds was the proud-spirited but ageing Laird of Kerse. Next to sending out his sturdy sons to harry the Kennedys, he enjoyed best sitting in the hall of Kerse Castle, before a banquet of venison haunch and flowing cup, recounting to kinsfolk and followers the glories of past victories and the infamies of his detested Carrick rivals. And his stories whipped up a rare hatred for the ancient foe.

On just such a night, three days short of Lammastide, when the waft of roasting meat was on the air, the tallows guttered and the company had grown mellow with good ale, a stranger pushed aside the crossed pikes at the entrance to the hall and boldly strode among them. When the feasting company recognised him as Gilbert Kennedy, a son of the ruling House of Carrick, hands whipped to hilts to take him.

'I come alone,' he announced proudly and in the strange, wayward chivalry of the age, they stayed their hands.

'What brings you here?' demanded Laird Craufurd, in reluctant admiration of the young man's foolhardiness to come among them like this, and briefly wondering if any of his own sons, bold though they were, would have done the same with the Kennedys.

'A message of defiance from the Kennedys.'

'Tell your defiance then.'

'My lord bids me tell you,' the young man's voice echoed from the stone walls with a hint of laughter in it, 'that on Lammas morning he will breach your soil to tether a sow pig on your land, Craufurd of Kerse, and that he and his Kennedy men will fight to the death to stop the Craufurds flitting her.' This was an original and provocative taunt without precedent and, half-infuriated half-intrigued, old Craufurd rose to the insult.

'You're a bardy callant, Gilbert Kennedy, to bring such a challenge to Craufurd of Kerse, but take you back my word on it to your lord that, though he bring armed Kennedys fae all the airts of Carrick to lead that precious sow-pig, it will not bide tethered on Kerse land.'

'Aye, that it will,' claimed Gilbert Kennedy, 'though every Craufurd north of the Doon shall try to flit it.'

The rules of tribal war demanded the challenger's safe conduct from Kerse that night and for the next three days there was a whetting of blades and a burnishing of shields. Strategy and counter-strategy were plotted and prepared on both sides of the river. Craufurd horsemen converged on the north bank from every outpost of Kyle, from Stewarton, Mauchline and the uplands of Muirkirk, while Kennedy horsemen gathered on the south bank, riding across moss hags where the whaups were crying, up from Girvan and across the hills from Barr and clattering up out of the grey High Street of Maybole.

Late on Lammas Eve the Kennedys, well armed and mounted on eager horses, massed in great high spirits for this saucy taunt to the Craufurds. Their lord and leader proudly surveyed his retinue, glittering there before him in the light of fitful camp-fires. The Craufurds, under old Kerse's son Esplin, determined to thwart the intended defilement of their land, camped across the river, pistols at their saddle-bows and hagbuts slung across their shoulders. They slept lightly, ready for the first move, set on doing their ancient laird proud and on taking back news to where his fiery spirit and frail body awaited the result of the day in Kerse Castle.

'Mind and not lay down your blades till that sow's flitted,' had been his last words to his beloved and stalwart sons before they left his chamber.

The two troops slept a few hours of the darkness through that long night and, though they were on the move before dawn, old Craufurd was already seated on a bench at Kerse, seeing in his mind's eye and hearing in his mind's ear, every move his men would make.

Now the battle was joined around the sow, which was under the hand of a swineherd lad. Axes were swung and cudgels thudded,

161

cries of triumph mingled with groans, and Craufurd met Kennedy in single combat. There were cleavered limbs and stunned heads. Horses plunged along the riverside which was fringed with alders, stumbling on spinning shields and shying away from quivering lances. And through it all flowed the good rich blood of decent Ayrshiremen, savage with pride. Now the Kennedys were across the Doon taking the fight, and the sow, into Craufurd territory. The herd, circled by brawny Kennedys, advanced warily looking for space clear of defenders where he could plant the sow that was to dishonour them. Bold men died to tether that bewildered pig and bold men died to turn it tail.

Esplin, heir to Kerse, saw his brother John, that most beloved of his father's sons, dashed to death by a Kennedy axe. Fury and grief roused him to a final rallying and ell by ell the tormenting Kennedys were pushed back towards the river. Finally, swimming and splashing on both sides of the small bridge, they backed across to their own side with the swineherd stumbling and tripping over the bloodied trotters of his sow.

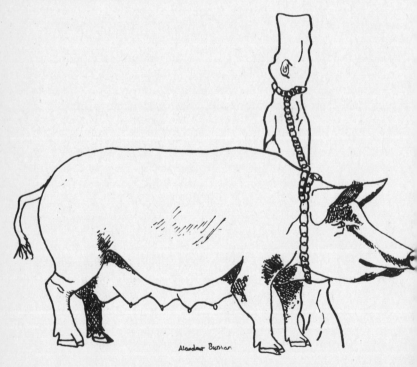

Decimated, the Kennedys fled in disorder over the bodies of their dead and dying. On the other side the Craufurds paused at the brink of the river and sadly counted what it had cost them to defy the enemy.

Back under the grey walls of his own keep sat old Craufurd of Kerse impatiently waiting word of the fighting. The thought of that Kennedy pig grunting on Kerse land maddened him and the thought of the dead was nothing to its rankle. Was, or was not, that sow moved? He refused the plaid a servant brought him against the cold, and threw down the broth they served him lest he took the ague . . . Was the sow flitted?

At last he spied a horseman riding hard across the moor and, half-dreading the tidings the courier brought, the old man struggled to his feet. The man reined in the horse and slid off over its steaming flanks.

'Is the sow flitted?' quavered Craufurd fearfully.

The messenger drew a nervous hand across his mouth. 'Alas, my word is sore, milord. Your son, the good John is dead and . . .' The old laird cut him short.

'But the sow? Is the sow flitted or no?' he demanded.

The courier looked at him wonderingly.

'Aye my laird . . . five score Kennedys are drowned in the Doon and half as many Craufurds lie dead on its banks . . . but aye . . . the sow is flitted.'

The old Laird of Kerse jumped up and did a gleeful dance.

'Then my thumb for John,' exulted the bereaved father '*The Sow is Flitted*'.

This story may be largely traditional but it was certainly accepted as reliable by Sir Alexander Boswell of Auchinleck, who was himself married-kin to the Craufurd family.

The Prophet of Sorn

There was a kind of stark romance about the Covenanting times when the outed ministers led psalm-singing and preached to faithful outdoor congregations in the Ayrshire hills and hollows. The whole cause gave rise later to a flood of highly emotive literature and minstrelsy. One has only to wander the kirkyards of south Scotland, to be told with great certainty that all of them were saintly martyrs, murdered by evil men, and that their cause had a total monopoly of the truth and of whatever godly men were living at the time.

There were godly men among them, for sure, and they may have had the edge over others in the matter of truth, but there were few rounded biographies of their outstanding men written by contemporaries or near successors. They were described in these accounts as pious, honest, fearless, outspoken, prayerful, bold and true-till-death ... Henderson, Johnstone, Renwick, Cargill, Cameron and Peden ... Peden now ... many's the tale told of the Prophet of Sorn, his hunting down, his exciting escapes, his moral stature, his comfortless ascetic days in the hiding-cave near his home, his powerful preaching from the mountain-side boulders known as Peden's Pulpits, his foretelling of the future. A giant of a man, Peden. And yet and yet ... tucked away in an ancient yellow, rought-cut book there is another glimpse of Peden seen perhaps by someone less than dazzled by his greatness.

John Brown, the carrier of Muirkirk, was an honest countryman, who knew the haunt of every moorland and burnside creature round his cot high up there on the Priesthill and who saw his God in every flower and tree. He had lived all his younger life so contentedly that he had never had to wonder whether or not he was happy. But today was his wedding day and he knew for sure that he was. His Isabel Weir was a dimpled, modest maid with cheeks the colour of briar roses and, in her collar and cap that were as white as the driven snow, she was the very picture of a Christian gudewife. And if a stolid fellow like the carrier could have said he was enchanted, he would have said it that day, enchanted with his bargain made when Master Alexander Peden had pronounced them man and wife. And Isabel too was smiling. She clung to her new man's arm, thanked the

164

Minister and told him demurely that she knew she and John would be very happy together, and with their bairns when they came.

Master Peden was the only one of the company who was not in good spirits and he brought a chill to the day before he left the house.

'Isabel Brown, be happy this day, and as long as ye may, for it's in my heart I must tell you that it's best you use your needle to lay by John's mort-clothes and dule-weeds for yoursel' instead of bairnies' frocks. For I'm feart it's them you'll need.'

He had left the cottage then, and Isabel near to weeping. John Brown kissed away her fears.

'He's a good man, Master Peden, but he's aye that gloomy and serious wi' his prophesyings. What's like to happen to me?'

Some years had passed now since that wedding day and children played about the cottage yard. John Brown was still the sedate and good living Christian he had always been. He had of late, however, taken to private prayer and Bible study or attending small farm kitchen services instead of going to the local Kirk, for these were more to his conscience than the new ways with the use of the English Prayer-book and the preaching of the young curate who had supplanted their own called minister.

But that simple change in his habit of worship was a rank offence in his King's eyes and one day while he was out digging peats for his cottage fire the dragoons came on him as a 'wanted' man, dragged him to his own door and called out his wife and bairns to the yard.

A dark figure, happed to the ankles in a hodden cloak, came out of the woods that had given him cover, and made his stealthy way towards the water of Ayr. Muirfowl rose before Alexander Peden's feet, he could see a heron hunched at the water's edge and fieldfare flocking across the stretch of land between. Every sound jangled Peden's nerves, he held his plaid up across his face when he whipped round from side to side as each one reached him. For the outed minister was a hunted fugitive. He looked all round again but there was no hiding place for a man on that wide moor, no growth bigger than a tuft of long-grown heather or broader than a single green rash. He would have to go back to the cottage at Priesthill where John Brown lived and which he had left himself that morning after a short stay. He had left in a hurry for word had come by a herd lad that the dragoons, under Claverhouse himself, were on the bleak slopes around Priesthill hunting him and enquiring also about Brown. Peden had fled. He was a power among the Covenanters, he told himself, and must not be taken. A rankling whisper in his heart told him that he shivered now, not from cold, but from fear of his life, and he stifled it under the pious reasoning that his work, for the right way to worship God, was not yet done. He had no notion what might have befallen Brown if he had been questioned but he supposed that he would find the carrier safe at Priesthill and ready to shelter him again. Peden approached the cottage carefully for fear the dragoons were still searching the moor.

All was quiet and he relaxed a little. He turned from the gable-end to the front of the house and stopped short at the sight of the blood-splashed white wall and the clump of tansy under it, crushed and broken where a man had surely fallen, shot by a squad. Now the silence was fearful and ominous, Peden trembled and stood still when he heard the sneck-bolt pulled back inside the door. He held up his cloak once more across his face, as the door opened no more than six inches wide. He saw Isabel Brown and dropped the mask. The woman's face was like carved marble and she gaped strickenly at the man who had wed her and her John not so many years since, but that she thought of now as a craven cowardly priest.

'Is your man at home?' he asked now, though he knew well enough that it was her man's blood that spattered the wall beside him.

'Come ben and see him,' she said bitterly.

He followed her inside and looked in silence at the still form on the floor where she pointed. She pulled back a plaid off the honest country face, and Peden too remembered the day he had married them.

'I warned you, mind, when you wed him, that you should lay by his winding sheet. It was surely ordained of God that he should die a martyr for the cause.' He tried to comfort her with the worth of her man's death. And she remembered again the great name he had for the second sight; 'Prophet Peden' they cried him in the South-West.

He prayed then, a long prayer, until she was weary and her frightened bairns fretting. And he was aware, all the time of it, that there was no resignation in her, for the unholy distaste she seemed to have for him.

'What happened?' he asked at last.

She wept then and told him brokenly of the scene she had found

166

when Claverhouse called her out to the yard. For it was Claverhouse himself, presently on a purge of rebels in Ayrshire and the South, who had led the troop at Priesthill ...

'Why do you not attend on the King's lawful curate at your church, John Brown?' Claverhouse had asked, from the height of his saddle.

'It's my conscience, I must obey my conscience rather than the King, if they're no' of the same mind,' explained the carrier mildly.

'You do not think that perhaps the King in his wisdom knows best what's right?' demanded Claverhouse.

'I dinnae ken the King's mind, but I ken the mind of God for John Brown.'

'Then best prepare yourself for death, for that's sedition and blasphemy,' the commander declared, and had the troopers thrust the carrier against his cottage wall.

They had shot him dead there before wife and children and put away their muskets, satisfied that Scotland was rid of yet another rebel.

'What think you now of your bonnie man?' Claverhouse had asked the stricken woman.

'I aye thought much of him, but never so much as I do now ...'

She finished the drawing of that sore picture and then turned on Peden.

'It was you. You wanted to leave that quick he had to get you away, so he was early out on the hill before his right time. It was your blame that the horse-soldiers with yon Clavers came on him there, and chased him or maybe dragged him home. And they shot him there where the tansy's bloodied, in front of my own eyes... and the bairns ... while you skulked in the woods and behind the bushes. You've maybe the gift of the foretelling, Master Peden, but you havenae the milk of human kindness nor the brave heart of a bit bird.' She buried her face in her bloodstained apron a moment and then spoke again.

'Were you at Pentland, or Bothwell Brig? No' you! You flit from farmhouse to hill-cot and from cave to garret, while others face it out so you can preach and prophesy.'

'I'm a man of God and of peace,' he said quietly, but he did not meet her eyes.

'My man was a man of the countryside, no' a sojer,' she answered him bitterly.

He left Priesthill scalded and shaken, maybe a better man for the flyting and anyway wishing with all his heart that he had been blessed with a greater share of courage and a smaller one of the second sight.

He had six more years to hap his plaid around him and flit about the moors and woodlands, outlawed for his cause. And whether or no there was ever any truth in the taunts wrung from Isabel Brown, that he was better than most at avoiding the dragoons, only God and Alexander Peden himself, Prophet of Sorn, knew for sure.

'Prophet' Alexander Peden, 1626-86, sometime schoolmaster, session clerk, precentor and minister, was born and reared in Sorn parish and after half a lifetime of being hunted across south-west Scotland, returned exhausted there to die. He was buried honourably at first in Auchinleck kirkyard but his grave was desecrated afterwards by Dragoons who buried him ignominiously at the foot of the Cùmnock gallows. Later the good citizens of the town retaliated by establishing the future position of Cumnock graveyard with the remains of Peden at its heart.

The Gypsy's Curse

It is not so very long ago, as folklore goes, since the trees round the ancient estate of Bargany near Dailly began to echo with the coarse calling of magpies and crows, nesting in the woods there, after a silence of nearly a century, during which these great birds were never heard or seen among their branches. Chilfies, bullfinch, field-fare and plover ... almost all the birds of moorland and copse sang and fluttered but nary a crow or magpie for nigh on a hundred years.

And they say that that magpie-silent, crowless century began one day when the harsh Laird of Bargany of the time was out riding round his estates, to threaten more work and higher multure payments from his unfortunate tenants. He was a broad, dark man with a proud beak of a nose, and his cold eyes glittered angrily when he saw an ancient gypsy woman limping along one of his pathways that day. The crone bobbed him a rheumaticky curtsey and smiled a cheerful, toothless smile.

'Milord!' she said agreeably. He might be stableman or visitor ... best be safe.

'What business have you on my land?' he demanded coldly.

'Good sir, I come to visit yonder big hoose to sell some geegaws to the Lady, for she's good to me and she'll buy a herb pillow and mibbee thread for her embroidery,' and she smiled at the thought of the bawbees the gentle milady would give her and the kind way she would bid the maidservant take her down to the kitchen for bannocks and a thick spreading of butter along with a jug of warm, spiced ale.

'Old woman you're naught but a beggar, and an Egyptian to boot, that dares to roam my land,' and he raised his whip to flick it across her shoulders.

But she jouked him and fled back along the path, leaving him with the whip dangling from his hand feeling foolish and angrier than ever. He spurred his mount and chased the old wife and caught her struggling in a thicket. Then he shamed himself and the good name of Bargany by thrashing her until she sobbed and throwing her down against a thorn tree by the path.

'And now get off my land and don't come disturbing me or the Lady Bargany with your fal-de-rals.' He turned his horse's head and

it pranced a moment before plunging back towards their meeting place and, as he went, he heard the old gypsy shout after him as she stumbled, snivelling, through the undergrowth, her shoulders still smarting from his beating.

'A curse on you this day my fine Lord Bargany . . . a curse on you and yours, for when the craws leave Bargany land this day they'll no' be back. There'll be lassies ... dochters to love and laugh with the good ladies of your hoose, but never a son and heir for its masters. No, Laird Bargany ... a curse ... a curse,' and she dragged herself out from the tangle of thorn, and shauchled across the rocky stretch that led down towards the river Girvan.

Bargany heard most of her malicious words, and the superstitious core, that was still deep set in staunch Presbyterian laird, as it was in simplest cotter, shivered inside Bargany, with his brave horsewhip tucked across his saddle.

And so it was ... just as the gypsy had foretold. Golden-haired girl-children romped in the glades and meadows round the keep, but its lairds were succeeded one after another by cousins, brothers and nephews for five generations and never a crow nor magpie did any of them see around Bargany in all that time.

Then one bright spring afternoon, shortly after the newest laird had taken up residence in the castle with his winsome bride, he was driving up the carriage way when, like his great-grand-uncle, he overtook a bent old gypsy wife shuffling along the hedgerow, her cloot of wares dangling from her hand.

'Good day to you, good wife,' he greeted her cheerfully and halted his horse beside her.

'What fine wares do you have there to show, a diamond necklace or ruby earrings maybe?' he bantered.

A gleam came into the gypsy's bead-black eyes as she knelt down to spread out her kerchief on the ground. The laird glanced over the pathetic little array of cheap trinkets and then at the sackcloth bindings that were her foot-gear. He selected a tangle of scarlet ribbons, and a handful of shells strung together to make a bracelet, and he smiled at the thought of such a gift for his dainty and well-tochered wife. Then he bade her to the kitchen for a good meal and pulled out his purse. He left her speechlessly turning over a gold coin in her thorny fingers and walking slowly towards the castle kitchen.

She came that way again the next New Year time, and found the village of Dailly rejoicing and celebrating the birth, at the castle, of the first son and heir born there in the lifetime of old Hew Kennedy, who had been a hundred years old at Martinmas. And as she looked up at the tall Bargany trees she saw two magpies flapping untidy wings, and half a dozen crows circling the sky round their topmost branches.

171

The Ayrshire Vendetta

In 1488, King James IV of Scotland put into execution a plan to establish peace and good government in the land by appointing local representatives to keep the peace on his behalf. This was done in Ayrshire as elsewhere and the first of these 'Bailies' in Cuninghame was Lord Glencairn.

After some years, however, the King removed the Bailieship from Glencairn and vested it instead in Lord Montgomerie of Eglinton. And it was this downgrading of Glencairn and, no doubt, the pride of Eglinton in his new position that gave rise to the long-lasting blood-vendetta between the two houses.

Glencairn showed his anger by a series of small insults and cattle-raids on Eglinton land, but the first serious offensive in the feud took place when Eglinton sent out a party of his men to Kerelaw Castle, one of Glencairn's several keeps, when its men-at-arms were not in residence. They plundered it and fired it until there was nothing of value left. The foray was swift and efficient and by nightfall Kerelaw Castle was no more than a blackened husk.

The Glencairns nursed their wrath and contented themselves for a year or two with further small irritant offensives, waylaying and stripping Eglinton messengers, firing their crops, filching their livestock and desolating the gardens of their womenfolk. A more serious incident when men from both factions were killed brought the intervention of the King. His arbiters reaffirmed that Eglinton was his chosen Bailie and Glencairn sulked the more dourly.

Although quarrels and confrontations littered the next few years and the sons of both houses were set upon from ambush and wounded...the young Master of Eglinton the more seriously...the main energy of both Glencairn and Eglinton factions for a time went into their common national duty of supporting the King in his defensive struggles, with arms and manpower. But throughout that period and the bitter and forlorn aftermath of the Battle of Flodden, when the King was killed and the cream of Scottish youth was lost, the two Ayrshire lords did not become reconciled.

Eglinton, smarting at the sight of his scarred son, struck the first grievous blow of the feud after Flodden and was responsible for the killing of two Glencairn lieutenants. Glencairn in his turn was

172

incensed at these deaths. He rode out from his castle at Kilmaurs to drive away his grief in the wind of the Cuninghame hills, but his fury remained. That he held close to his heart and when he came on a hill overlooking Eglinton Castle he reined in and looked long at his rival's ancestral home.

Two days later Glencairn rode out with a troop from Kilmaurs Castle on a trail of destruction such as had never been seen before among these gentle hills and burns of South Ayrshire. Their express intent was to pillage and raze crops, to fire the homes of helpless retainers and small tenant holders. They wreaked havoc on gear, equipment, horses and other stock and left smouldering lanes behind them of what had been corn rigs, blackened and wasted. Then they put torches to the barns of Eglinton and finally to the Castle itself. Nothing survived, of oak floors or fine carved ceiling, of tapestries, paintings or ornaments and in the archives the Charter to Montgomerie lands and other family records and documents, preserved since the Norman Conquest, were tinder to the fire.

Again revenge was delayed because the strength of both factions had to be thrown behind the new King in his struggles. That Earl of Eglinton died and so did that Glencairn. The two Masters became the opposing Earls and for a time had enough to do serving Scotland and seeing the Reformed religion established.

But the hatred never quite died down and a new round of clashes disturbed the peace of Cuninghame. One day in 1586 Hugh, the 4th Earl of Eglinton, set out to attend the Royal Court at Stirling. He rode peaceably with only unarmed attendants and looked forward with pleasure to fulfilling an engagement to dine at Lainshaw House near Stewarton. Lainshaw was an old friend to the Eglinton family and a kindly man, so Earl Hugh travelled confident that Lady Lainshaw, who had been born a Glencairn, would as Lainshaw's wife have thrown off the unlikeable characteristics of her clan and welcome him with warmth and a fine dinner. Her invitation had certainly been most pressing.

But Margaret Lainshaw had not shed her old loyalties. A white napkin fluttered at a high window of Lainshaw House signalling to a band of over thirty armed Glencairn retainers hidden in the wooded approaches, that Earl Hugh was in sight with only a handful of attendants. Eglinton and his group were taken by surprise, overpowered and, the records say, the men were hacked to death. Hugh himself was first put to the sword and then shot dead.

There was an outcry from the whole countryside, drawing outright denial from Glencairn of any personal part in the killing. Few believed him and certainly not the Master of Eglinton, Hugh's brother and heir.

Outraged cottars and biener tenants, who had previously been inclined to let the gentry fight their own squabbles, flocked to the new Earl's side to avenge the late one. And they scoured the shire for Glencairn men, whether of the murder-band or not. There were pursuits and assaults, threats, flights and killings and the leader of the assassins was himself run to earth hiding in a chimney far away in Hamilton and quickly despatched.

As for the inhospitable Lady Lainshaw, she lived in total seclusion for many years in a house at Pearce Bank, never permitted even to walk in its gardens and only later, when life had quietened in Cuninghame did she come quietly home to Lainshaw to live in retirement. And never again in the whole of her life did she show her face to a Montgomerie of Eglinton.

It had seemed to some who were weary of it all that the blood feud of Cuninghame would never end. But the power of the Crown was growing and the arm of the law becoming stronger over the lawless lords of the West. Resentment trickled down the generations, it was true, but it never again boiled over into the war of no quarter it had been for nearly a hundred years.

An account of the killing of the young Earl of Eglinton from *The Historie of King James the Saxth* suggests that Lady Lainshaw had a principal accomplice in Cuninghame of Robertland, a 'very dear friend' of the murdered Earl, who had loved this youth 'as his own bedfellow'. It is suggested that during the whole of their intimate friendship Cuninghame was plotting Earl Hugh's death.

STUART HAYNES.

The Puzzling of Jinny Willock

Once upon a time, it's said by a Loudon valley lady who had the tale from her grandmother, there lived in a top garret in Newmilns a worthy citizen of that weaving and lace-making town. His life-work was to collect the snippings from the undersides of stuffs on the loom and take them away in his horse-drawn cart.

He was, says the story-teller, what in those supposedly prim and mealy-mouthed days, was called a Jinny-Willock.

'A queer person,' she whispers, 'with skin like a flower-petal, no stubble, never even down, and a high-pitched voice.' But in spite of all these gentle characteristics Jinny Willock had apparently the manly habit of getting as drunk as a lord at Nannie's ale-house most Saturday evenings after work. The halflin drinkers who had known him all their young lives as a harmless village eccentric, mocked him without malice and always led him gently home to his garret after his weekly toping had left him incapable of finding it himself.

But there came a time when his over-fancy for a dram seemed like to do him a mischief and young Doctor Stirrat, who patronised the same ale-house, minded him again and again that he was liquoring himself into an early mortkist.

He had spoken quite seriously to the snippings-man once more on the Saturday night of this story but the old man was beyond taking-in the warning. His head was on his arms on the table and as usual the two Cooper lads and the giant callant Hew Dandie emptied their own pint stoups, sighed, and while two oxtered him outside, the third unhitched the old man's horse and cart and the little procession creaked and clopped and trailed along the road to Jinny Willock's entry.

The usual procedure was to take the horse out of the shafts, take her through to the small back yard and leave the cart tipped up against the wall at the front. Then they would carry the helpless Jinny up the narrow spiral of stone stairs to the bare little attic with its wall-bed, chair and small, square, barred winnock.

That night Jinny was laid safely on his bed senseless as usual, to sleep off the effects of his night out and be ready for the Kirk in the morning. And then Geordie Cooper had his brainwave.

The three tiptoed down the stair and brought the horse back

through the entry from the yard and with much stifled laughter coaxed her protesting up the garret stair. The horse whinnied and clattered but nothing wakened Jinny Willock and eventually they had the animal in the tiny room, tethered to the window-bars, with her head beside her master's bed.

Then they crept downstairs again and spent a cheerful and busy half-hour dismantling the cart, wheels, shafts, sides and bottom of which they carried carefully into the entry and up the stairs. Another happy half-an-hour was spent putting the thing together again so that, when they left Jinny Willock snoring unsuspectingly in the wall-bed, in the room keeping him company, was his horse and cart.

He was a puzzled man, nay a frightened man, at his own cleverness when he woke up in the morning to find Betsy's head on the pillow beside him. He spent the time of the sermon that day wondering, not only how he had got the horse and cart up the winding stair, but how on earth he would ever get it down again.

No one can say just how he did it, nor whether Jinny Willock risked his health and reason by going back to the ale-house, ever again.

The Devil and the Irish Maid

There was consternation in the Montgomerie pantry. The young Mistress, wife to General Robert Montgomerie, was expecting her aristocratic in-laws, the Earl and Countess of Eglinton, to pay a visit to her Irvine home, and the word had just come up from her steward that a number of small but valuable pieces of table and ornamental silver were missing.

The steward, a trusted long-term servant, suggested that a new Irish serving-maid had stolen them and he brought her upstairs to face her master and mistress. The story goes that, although there were a dozen other servants, the accusation against the maid was put bluntly and without any expressions of doubt, and that Irish temper rose in the girl at what she said was injustice.

'Sure I never laid a finger on your silvers, Mistress, and I'll find the one that did, though I have to raise the Devil himself.'

Robert Montgomerie admitted to himself that they had been hasty to lay blame so certainly, without more evidence, and he let the girl's ungodly outburst pass as rash Irish anger. She was sent downstairs again, while they considered further how to discover the real culprit, if this girl was speaking the truth and was innocent.

But the maid had meant what she said, and was seen by others to go down into the laigh cellars with a Bible, a riddle and a handful of feathers. A gossiping watcher saw her drawing a circle round herself on the loose earth of the cellar floor and turn the riddle round it on end, anti-clockwise, all the while with nine black feathers in her hand that she had pulled from the tail of a black cock. Then she read Psalm 51 and a verse from Chapter 19 of Revelation. This cantrip material-ised the figure of the Devil himself, risen half out of the ground dressed in seaman's clothing with a dark blue cap. The spy then told how the Devil asked the maid what she wanted of him.

She put her question and when he answered it she cast three of her black feathers on him and bade him back where he had come from. At this he disappeared into the earth.

The girl then read the verse from Revelation backwards, and Satan this time rose from the floor with one leg above the ground. After further question and answer the maid discarded three more feathers at him and he subsided and sank. A third time, after the backward reading from the Revelation, he rose again right out of the ground in

177

black now, with a long black tail. A third question, three more feathers cast at him and then Satan disappeared altogether. The whole house shuddered, whether at his departure or with the thunderstorm raging outside, and the clipe was carried to the General of the ongoings in his cellars.

There was a hideous howling of the town's dogs, and milkmaids told later how the very goats they were milking dried up on the spot, at exactly the time that the Irish serving maid was called again to see her master and mistress. She entered their sitting-chamber, whey-faced and shivering and told them that she had had of the Devil the name of the thief of the household silver.

'Say the name!' ordered Montgomerie sternly. She said it and told them also that the pieces were hidden in a kist under the bed of another servant.

There the silver was found as she had said. But the master was by now more concerned that he had apparently a witch-girl meddling with Satan in his service, than that he had a common thief whose truck was only with her own greed. The 'witch' was sent to prison to be dealt with after the Eglinton visit was safely over.

Legend does not tell of her torture or browbeating, only that she confessed to having studied black arts from a Doctor Colvin, a man learned in magic herbal potions brewed from the Irish countryside, and in the incantations needed to materialise the Devil himself.

'The Hellish Art of Riddle-turning' was a recognised thief-finding device. A list of names was chanted as an ordinary riddle was rolled along on its edge and when the thief's name was spoken the riddle was said to tremble and fall.

178

The Stickit Minister

Young Mungo Reid had romped through his schooldays absorbing his English and Latin lessons as easily as Mathematics. He had, in addition to his brains, the kind of innocent presence and resounding voice which his widowed mother and grandmother were quite convinced were made for the Scottish pulpit and would find fulfilment nowhere else. That a Christian minister might want certain other gifts and graces simply did not occur to them, and accordingly Mungo was groomed for 'the cloth'.

Being the natural scholar that he was, it was never necessary for him to be a studious hermit in his rooms near the university, and deny himself the ordinary pleasures and company of healthy young manhood. And so he was able, while he pursued his studies, not only to galravaitch merrily with his fellows, but to woo bonnie Mary Blythe from the next parish when he was at home for holidays.

Mary's father was an upstanding elder of the Kirk, a Justice of the Peace and a merchant rich as Croesus. Anyway, with his heavy gold watch-chain and pearl tie-pin, so he seemed to Mungo, who was hard put to it to find a change of stockings on a Sabbath morning.

Their families decided gravely among themselves that, before Mungo was settled in a charge and started on the preaching, he and Mary should marry. It was common knowledge they agreed, nodding their heads wisely, that a young single minister was the target of every unwed female in his own parish and every other bordering it.

On the eve of the day their banns were to be cried in the Kirk, Mungo arrived at Mary's house in his best dark suit (actually his only suit, dark or otherwise) looking fresh and earnest and every inch the pastor. He charmed his bride's aunts by his shy quips and attentive manners. He handed round tea and scones without knocking over small tables or spindly chairs, so deftly in fact, that they could not help remarking what an asset he would be at church meetings. Mungo satisfied Mary's papery uncles too by talking seriously of his studies and his admiration for his professors at the college.

After tea and scones, came a round of Mistress Blythe's cakes and home-made berry wine, said to be very mild and quite inocuous but nevertheless sipped very slowly by all the guests. Except Mungo.

179

He found the wine most palatable, thoroughly pleasing and much better without the cakes; and if he had been refilling his glass as often with his hostess's equally excellent lemonade she would have been flattered indeed by his appreciation. After he had had four or five glasses of the wine, however, Mary's mother was not a bit flattered at what came next. Mungo had by now forgotten where he was, and had some idea coming and going hazily in his mind, that he was with his student friends in Edinburgh. All might yet have been saved, for a month or two anyhow, if he had not in a luckless moment thrown inhibition to the wind and stunned the company by ordering the good-room table to be pulled aside. Perhaps, the bride's mother hoped desperately, he was going to make a betrothal speech or witness to the seriousness with which he was to pursue his ministry, and life at the manse with Mary.

But, instead, he took the floor, turned three somersaults, stood on his hands and congratulated himself in very colourful language quite unbecoming a shepherd of the flock.

The embarrassed and shocked aunties drifted away on hushed feet after that, only one twinkle-eyed old bird lingering in the guilty hope that there might be a repeat performance. But she gave up that hope and sighed a little when she saw James Blythe bundling his daughter's 'intended' out of the back door and closing it after him with a righteous slam. Mary, it seemed, was well-rid of such a scoundrel.

But Mary too had been as blithe as her name. And what scunnered her godly father altogether and finally took the Edinburgh University Divines, already dubious about Master Reid's total commitment to his calling, into solemn conclave, was the arrival in the Ayrshire parish somewhile later, of an apple-cheeked laddie, the spit image of Mungo.

Mungo changed his life's direction and became a successful schoolmaster. Whether Mary Blythe was the dominie's wife and helpmeet records do not tell, but do say that young Dandie Reid was reared by the twinkle-eyed aunt, decently deep in the country.

Wheeliejean and the Laird's New Bride

In the olden days when ploughing, stooking, wooing, baking and even kirking, all had patron faeries ... when the Habitrots and Bobbinancies of the Border shires and the East of Scotland were the kindred sisters of Mistress Wheeliejean of Ayrshire and the West.

Wheeliejean was none of your gossamer web-winged golden-haired wee folk with a glimmer halo round her as she moved. She took the form of an old wife, plain as a pikestaff, but kind and clever, and at hand whenever a weary spinster got her yarn or her doings into a fankle.

A good mortal woman of Kyle had a winsome daughter called Kirsty, who had no great fancy for work and who was ever ready to wander by the sun-spangled streams of summer, the grey sad water's edge of winter, or among the summer's poppies and harebells and raggy-robin flowers, than do her stint of the day's labours.

Her mother scolded and entreated. The bonnie lass would mean to mend her ways but always forgot and took to the countryside again. At last the good wife lost her temper and told the girl she would give her seven days to fill seven creels with yarn from her flax or else she would cast her out for ever from her home.

Every day when her mother went off to clean at the laird's house, the girl started on her task. But her hands, though gentle with the animals of the riverbank and deft at gathering and arranging wild flowers, were clumsy and unskilled at the spinning and she could not fill one creel in half the week, never mind seven. In despair she left her wheel and ran out to compose herself among the ferns along the burnside and wonder how she would fare without a home. She wept as she wandered and then found that her elbow was grasped by an old woman, bright eyed and smiling, whom she had never seen in the vicinity before. She said her name was Wheeliejean and she led Kirsty willy-nilly back to the girl's room in the cot, sat down on her stool and began to spin. Higher and higher bundled the yarn into the creels until four of them were full. Gleefully Kirsty took up the fine spinnings and hanked them, and when she looked round to thank her she found that the old woman had vanished. Minding her manners and wanting to show her gratitude (and maybe thinking to have her back to fill the other three creels) Kirsty ran out after the faery and caught a wispy glimpse of her as if she was walking in a mist along the riverside and into a clump of dark trees. Kirsty followed her softly into the woodland and there saw, in a clearing with cold light slanting into it through the trees, a group of a dozen other women of all ages sitting with their spinning-wheels. Their quick, nimble fingers and hands danced as they worked and whether they were young or old, their faces were calm and beautiful like those of holy women.

Kirsty crept silently away wondering how she could finish her task alone and wishing that she had such hands herself. But the next day, and the next, and the next when she waved her mother off to work, she went in and found Wheeliejean already busy with the spinning.

'How can I thank you? How can I repay you, for I have no silver or gold?'

'Dinnae try, my bonnie, dinnae try ... and never ever tell who spun your yarn, or me and my sisters will never can help another poor mortal creature like yourself.'

So pleased was Kirsty's mother when she saw the hanks of yarn, that the young laird, riding by, heard her cry of joy that the girl had at last worked so hard and she had these fine creels of yarn. Now it happened that the laird was just then looking for a wife who would be a fine spinster and keep him well-supplied with clothes for his back. When he heard how much she had spun that week and saw how winsome and gentle she was too, he woo'd and won Kirsty who had always admired him from afar and, now that she knew him, loved him very much. But she was greatly afraid that she would fail him as a spinster.

A week after their marriage she was sitting worrying at her problem, not a bit like the happy creature she was naturally, when Wheeliejean came by, 'tut-tutted' and promised to help her yet again.

'Bring your braw bridegroom to yonder woodland where you'll see me with my spinning sisters, and just bid him look at our faces as we work. And ... dinnae let on we're friends, you and me.'

Next day the young laird, in a handsome crimson coat, and his lady, in a flower-sprigged dress, walked along the riverside and looked in the clearing among the dark trees. But this time, instead of the kind, beautiful and contented faces of Wheelijean's sisters Kirsty saw thirteen ugly-faced crones with crooked noses and thick lips, with squinting eyes and no teeth, and with red-rough hands, and fingers like gnarled twigs.

182

Wheeliejean heard Kirsty and her husband gasp with horror and came towards them. Even her bright eyes were dull, her once-rosy cheeks blae and weathered.

'Good day to you, friends. Bid you come and meet my sisters.'

The laird spoke to each of them, one by one, and shuddered at their ugliness.

'Be not afraid. 'Tis caused only by the spinning. They're good women at heart and cannae help the squinting and bending over their work. The smell of the yarn too, twists them so.' She turned to Kirsty and spoke past her to the laird. 'Mind you never let this pretty bride near to a spinning wheel if you love her bonnie looks.'

The laird truly loved more than Kirsty's bonnie looks, but he did like them too, and his arm tightened round her waist. He vowed that nary a wheel would he ever allow near her. And he never did.

Kirsty never spun, nor laboured over household task, for there were servants who loved her and served her well. But she made her lord a fine wife in other ways and was ever a bright jewel at his table when he entertained. She gathered armsful of the flowers and ferns she found by streams and hills on his estates, and filled the dark corners of his house with them. In time too she filled that house with children too. The boys were all handsome and brave. None of the girls could spin but they had many other accomplishments and sewed beautiful tapestries. And when they were still quite young she took them to meet with kind Wheelijean and her changeful sisters of the woodland clearing.

Peep into a Parish School

*(Extracts from the Logbook of Girvan School kept
during the Session 1863-64)*

August 31	Nine pupils have gone to other schools, alleged reason being dissatisfaction with the allotment of prizes at end of previous session.
September 18	School closed at 3 p.m. for marriage of Lord Ardmillan's daughter. School Cricket Club met to arrange tomorrow's match with non-members from this and the Charity School. Arrangements made for the repair of the school football.
September 23	Unusual number of scholars absent today — probable cause, the eating of fruits.
October 7	A good deal of punishing today for want of lessons.
October 8	Severity has borne good fruit today in the better-said lessons, and the strap has been 'laid in lavender' for a time.
October 14	This being the day of Girvan Cattle Show the pupils petitioned yesterday that it might be given as a holiday. Master consented on condition of their making up for it some Saturday soon.
October 17	(Saturday) This day the school met for Wednesday's holiday. Very few were absent and lessons were well said. Master left at half past eleven to go to funeral. Pupil teachers instructed to dismiss at 12 noon.
October 27	A good deal of strapping today for carelessness in writing. The master would note here that although he could keep the school at its present state without corporal punishment he cannot get the same amount of progress out of some boys without a touch of the strap occasionally.
November 17	In thinking over the day's work, master finds nothing noteworthy.

November 19	Practice of examining hands of Junior Division of pupils and condemning the two dirtiest to bring in coals and water, seems to work well.
December 8	Weather very stormy, vents not drawing well, which made school uncomfortable. Rain also came in the ceiling.
December 18	Anticipation of Christmas holidays begins to peep out.
December 21	Discipline becoming somewhat lax as master thinks it useless to have recourse to severe measures so near a vacation.
January 20	Cane purchased yesterday cannot be found today. The master sent for other two and intimated that nothing else would be used for punishing until missing cane accounted for.
January 25	This was one of those days in which everything goes wrong and nobody can tell why. Very hands of clock went back instead of forward.
May 12	Bathing has become favourite midday occupation of boys. Master thought it his duty to prevent the little girls from the Charity School from wading among the bathers but was met by a storm of virulent opposition from the former.
May 25	School dismissed today at 3 o'clock to let children see a travelling menagerie, to which admitted at a penny each.
May 30	Master, having ascertained that an absentee had been sent to school in the morning, despatched two officers of justice to apprehend the truant. The latter, however, having espied them in the distance got safely ensconced under the blanket and his too compassionate Mamma refused to give him up.
May 31	Yesterday's truant appeared this morning repentant and was thought sufficiently punished with disgrace and making up lost time.
July 28	Examination and presentation of prizes. Vacation till 29th August.

The Public Wooing

Some two hundred years ago one of the employees in the Ayr Town Office was much concerned to find a suitable husband for a plain and unhousewifely sister. He kept his ear to the ground for the chance of hearing of a possible suitor who might be encouraged. At last in an ale-house one evening he heard tell of a simple young man of Ayr, one Arthur Crookshank, who was likewise on the look-out for a steady wife.

The brother, William Weir, began a cautious correspondence with Arthur, writing, then later speaking, highly of his sister's charms and accomplishments. It scarcely mattered to the bashful Arthur that the claims were extravagant. It was enough of a miracle that a well-set-up man thought him worth courting. He laboured long under a plethora of tallows, lettering out laborious replies, and the wooing by proxy progressed with apparent satisfaction to all concerned. Eventually, without bride and groom having clapped eyes on one another, a wedding was arranged. The ceremony was to be in Tarbolton where the bride's brother found a minister prepared to overlook the odd circumstance, and to Tarbolton therefore, on a day of summer with the sun flooding the hedgerows and fields, Arthur set out to meet his bride for the first time and, within a quarter hour of the meeting, to take his vows to cherish her for life. The procession of young men which kept him company on the journey was dressed in its Sabbath best with Kilmarnock bonnets and bright coloured kerchiefs, and a merry boisterous retinue they made. Eight hundred, they said, came from all airts round Kilmarnock and Tarbolton to witness the meeting and uniting of this odd couple. A good-humoured noisy band of intimates carried him on their shoulders from home and then oxtered him along the road to Fail Toll to meet his bride Miss Minnie Weir.

At the moment of meeting they eyed each other without expression. The guests encircled the couple who now walked side by side. Some cheered, some fiddled and some played the flute as the Minister arrived in their midst to bid them to his church.

Those who could, crowded into the kirk and fell silent briefly while the Minister made them man and wife. The rest waited patiently outside and raised more cheers when Mister and Mistress Crookshank emerged together.

Then the whole party set off on the long walk to Ayr to celebrate at the old Blue Bell Inn. Ale flowed and spirits were high and various travellers and packmen joined the wedding party when it took over the inn and the yard outside. One well-lathered pedlar, blear of eye and maudling with sentimental good wishes, took quite a notion to the bride. He balanced himself against Arthur's chair and leered into Minnie's face. Then he turned to Arthur.

'I'll tell you what, shir ... I've a fair fanshy for thish exquishite creature. I'll gie you one whole pound shterling for her. I'll buy her off you.'

Arthur had been a mite less boisterous than all his well-wishers, ever since he had first laid eyes on his bride, for the truth was he had believed her brother's highly coloured and glowing tributes and had expected a much more ravishing creature than the dumpy wee buddy with the snub nose who was now Mistress Crookshank. He felt he had ben sold short. And besides he had taken a good stoup of ale and a few chasers of spirits ...

'Done!' he said so emphatically that Minnie, in a pique, retaliated by almost leaping with indecent haste to the pedlar's side, indicating to Arthur that he had not come up to expectations either and that she was delighted to be rid of him. The bargain was struck and the couple separated.

Next morning the pedlar took his sore head away out of the district with his second-hand wife; Arthur went back to his old daily round and heard nothing of Minnie for well-nigh two years.

And then one day in early summer without warning she arrived at his cottage door tattered, white-faced and wretched. The pedlar had tired of her and put her out while he went off stravaiging over the countryside to sell his wares with another wench. The simple kind-hearted Arthur, who had not succeeded in finding a replacement, took her in and opened his mother's old clothes kist to her, to clad herself decently again. Next morning he went off to work whistling and looking forward to coming home in the evening to a clean swept hearth and a hot sup.

But by evening when he reached home the door was lying open and she was gone, along with blankets, plaids, pewters, looking-glass and his best horn spoons. The house had been ransacked of all that was worth a bawbee.

And over the hills towards Ochiltree, Minnie and her pedlar were pushing their handcart, laughing softly at the thought of the gullible Arthur looking round his empty house.

The Shifting of Stewarton Kirk

The window neuk in the Stewarton Inn was the usual gathering corner of the four worthies of that town, Tam, Davie and the Watt brothers, Malky and Jamuck. Most nights they finished their crack while it was still at the sensible stage and took their separate and steady ways home. And they would have claimed that the night when this incident took place was no different from any other.

It was a summer evening, long light with a gentle sun not yet westering low, and there was a fair amount of clash to be chewed over, gossip about the village, the weaver work and their various families. Malky and Jamuck, for instance had just set up their machines to make a quantity of nightcaps ordered by a local store, when an urgent demand had come from the army for soldiers' outdoor and 'undress' bonnets. The Colonel, or whoever had ordered these, could have placed his list with a Kilmarnock firm but seemingly had the sense to prefer the superior article made in Stewarton and must not be disappointed, whatever the inconvenience. Tam's worry was more serious, for his daughter, a gentle-reared girl, who had been brought up to know right from wrong perfectly well, was wilful set on wedding yon Donald Doaks, the apprentice to the smith, and so outwith the Bonnet Craft Guild altogether. It would have been bad enough if the lad had just been in a different Bonnet Guild, but the villain was to be a smith and, since his lass was stubborn, and the boy and his kin all set on the match, Tam feared it would come to a fist fight. And Davie nodded gravely that it very likely would.

Those and suchlike concerns were the gist of their chat over the first few rounds of the evening. But weaving-shop and family troubles gave them a thirst and as the time wore on, long silences fell on the four cronies as they slaked it.

It was Malky Watt, tucked in closest to the winnock, who raised the first alarm about the state of symmetry of the Stewarton Kirk as he saw it framed in the glass.

'Tam ... Davie, see here. Look Jamuck, the kirk's no' sittin' right. It's no' square to the street.'

One after the other they looked through the window. Their focussing was not altogether sharp, but they agreed gravely, all four, that either in its first building or as a result of a storm, or maybe a current in the ground under it, their parish kirk was not now set due east to west.

This was a much more serious matter to good Presbyterian citizens than a steering girl's mismatching or overworked looms in the weaving shop.

'We'll have to shift it,' declared Tam firmly. The others nodded. They sat there and arranged their strategy to rectify the shame on Stewarton's architecture. It was lucky there were four of them. They downed another dram to give them strength, wiped their mouths purposefully with the backs of their powerful hands and strode with deliberate straightness up the little street.

Each man went to his allotted corner of the kirk building and bent down to grasp it at the base.

'To the right a wee pickle, Tammas,' shouted Jamuck.

'No, no, too much . . . easy left, twa-three inches, Malky.' They sweated and heaved until they were red-faced and grunting, but Jamuck was not satisfied until he left his corner, walked round the building and cocked an eye at each side from ground to sky.

'Just there, just there,' he said at last. And the others stepped back to admire their work. Except Davie. He was still bent down at his corner.

'Ech dear, whatna thing! We've set it down on my coat tail,' he lamented loudly. 'We'll have to ease it up a bit again.'

Soberly they bent to the task and for half an hour they laboured. Davie took his foot off his own coat tail to tip up his corner of the kirk with his toe. He was free.

'That's me now,' he called to the others. 'I'm clear.' This time they all stood back well satisfied with their work and glowing with the joy of service done for the parish.

And then Tam, Davie, Jamuck and Malky were agreed that they deserved another stoup for their efforts, and walked slowly down the road again to the Inn.

Glossary

Abune Above
Ackyfortis Nitric acid
Airts Directions
An If
Ash Ash-stick
Auld Old

Back-end Latter part of
    year
Bairn Child
Banns Public intimation
    of intention to marry
Bardy Bold
Bawbee Halfpenny
Bawdy Humorously
    indecent
Ben Inner room
    (come ben)
Bide Stay
Bien Well-to-do
Big Build (v)
Blae Purplish blue (adj.)
Blatting Blustering
    (v, adj.)
Bogle Hobgoblin
Bokey Sick (adj.)
Boss Raised stud (n)
    empty (adj.)
Braw Handsome (adj.)
Bruit Noise (v)
Bung Stopper
Burn Stream
Burrier Hangman
Byke Wasp-nest (n), Bees

Cadge Cart (v)
Callant Lad (n)
Caller Fresh
Canny Careful
Cantrip Magic, mischief
Cauld Cold
Chaff Strawfilled mat
Chaw Chew
Chawner Mutter (v)
Chilfie Chaffinch
Chink Space
Chittering Chattering
Clachan Hamlet

Clash Gossip (n or v)
Cleek & gird Hook &
    hoop (plaything)
Clipe Tale-tell
Clod-hopper Bumpkin
Coggie Bowl
Compear Appear on
    summons
Coof Fool
Corp Body

Daft Silly
Dander Stroll (n or v)
Darge Labour (n or v)
Dawdle Dally
Dited)
Doited) Stupid
Dominie Schoolmaster
Doo Dove, pigeon
Dour Sullen
Douse Extinguish or
    throw water over
Dowy Sad
Dramming Drinking
    whisky
Dreich Tedious, dull
Drouthy Thirsty
Dreep Drop down
Dule Mourning
Dule-weeds Mourning
    clothes
Dule tree Tree for
    hanging or meeting to
    make decisions
Dwam Daze (n)
Dyke Wall

Ell thirty-seven inches

Fankle Tangle (v or n)
Far-ben Well-in
Farl Oaten cake
Fee Hire
Flee Fly (v)
Flitting Removing
Flummox Confound
Forbye Also
Furth Outwith

Fyke Fret or Bustle

Gallivant)
Galravaitch) Gad about
Gauger Exciseman
Gawp Gape
Gear Effects, Possessions
Glammer Spell (n)
Glaur Mud
Gibbet Gallows
Girny Complaining
    (adj.)
Gist Drift (n)
Gorse Whin Furze
Graith Harness (n)
Grieve Farm overseer
Guddle Grope with
    hands, often for fish
Gudewife Housewife
Gudeman Man-of-house
Gude-son   )
    -daughter) in law
    -sister   )

Halflin Youth
Hagbut Gun
Hags Moss, Bog
Hap Wrap
Ha'porth Halfpenny-
    worth
Hard-by Near
Heeshie-baw Cradle (v)
Heuches Hollows, Pits
Hinder Deter
Hinterland Inland
Hirpling Limping
Hirsel One-man herd
Hodden Drab woven
    cloth
Hogmanay New Year's
    Eve
Hone Sharpen (v)
Howff Inn
Hoyden Tomboy
Hummock Hillock
Hunner Hundred
Hurdies Buttocks & hips

191

Ingle Fire

Jouk Avoid by stooping under — Dodge

Kailpatch Vegetable garden
Keek Peep
Keep Castle
Kelpie River-demon, Sprite
Ken Know
Kenspeckle Easily recognised
Kirk Church
Kirtle Woman's outer garment

Laigh Low
Laird Landlord-owner
Lave Rest
Let on Divulge
Lo'e Love
Lobby Hallway
Loof Palm
Luckenbooth Locking-booth
Lum Chimney

Makar Poet
Maudling Sentimental
Maun Must
Mavis Thrush
Mirk Gloom, Darkness
Mite Little (n)
Mort-clothes Shroud
Mort-kist Coffin
Muckle Much, great
Multure Portion to the laird or his miller

Nary Never
Nether Lower
Neuk Nook

Oot Out
Outed Ousted
Outfield Uncultivated area, grazing land

Oxter Armpit

Parritch Porridge
Pawky Slyly humorous
Peasweep Lapwing
Pinkie Smallest finger
Plover Lapwing
Pooch Pocket
Pouter-pigeon Large cropped pigeon
Put about Bothered (adj.)

Quean Attractive girl

Ranting Boisterous
Rash Rush (n)
Reiving Thieving
Rig Ridge (corn growing)
Rime Hoar frost
Rump Tail-end

Sark Shirt
Scart Scratch (v)
Scrivener Scribe
Scunner Disgust (v or n)
Sennight Week
Shauchling)
Shaughling) Shambling
Shirpit Shrunken, puny
Shoon Shoes
Shouthers Shoulders
Siccar Certain
Siller Silver
Skeely Skilful
Skelp Smack
Sklim Climb nimbly
Skirl Shriek
Skliff Shuffle feet
Slavering Dribbling from mouth
Smirr Drizzle (n or v)
Smit Infect or infection
Sneck Bolt (lock)
Snell Keen, cold
Sojer Soldier
Sonsy Buxom, comely
Souter Shoemaker
Southron One from south, 'English'

Spaewife Woman who foretells
Spiel Speech
Spier Ask
Spirtle Pot-stick
Spume Spray (sea) (n)
Stane Stone
Steering Stirring, restless
Stickit Failed, stuck
Stooking Stacking (v)
Stint Allotted share of work
Stoup Vessel for liquid
Stravaig Wander boldly
Swig Mouthful of liquid

Taffy Toffee
Tallow Candle
Tatterdemalion Ragged
Tawse Punishment strap
Thibbet Coarse woven cloth
Thirled Enslaved
Thrawn Stubborn
Tocher Dowry
Toper Drinker
Toon, Toun Town
Trig Neat
Tryst Meet or meeting (v or n)

Vennel Alley

Wae Woebegone
Waly Clever
Warlock Wizard
Whaup Curlew
Wheen Lot, much
Whiles Sometimes
Whinge Whine
Whippet Racing dog
Wight, wite Strongman
Winnock Window

Yill Ale
Yin One
Yirdfast Stuck in the earth
Yon That, there